## World University Library

The World University Library is an international series
of books, each of which has been specially commissioned.
The authors are leading scientists and scholars from all over
the world who, in an age of increasing specialisation, see the
need for a broad, up-to-date presentation of their subject.
The aim is to provide authoritative introductory books for
university students which will be of interest also to the general
reader. The series is published in Britain, France, Germany,
Holland, Italy, Spain, Sweden and the United States.

# Hans Freudenthal

# Mathematics
# Observed

translated from the German
by Stephen Rudolfer and I.N.Baker

**World University Library**

McGraw-Hill Book Company
New York Toronto

© Hans Freudenthal 1967
Translation © George Weidenfeld and Nicolson Limited 1967
Library of Congress Catalog Card Number: 65-23826
Phototypeset by BAS Printers Limited, Wallop, Hampshire, England
Printed by Officine Grafiche Arnoldo Mondadori, Verona, Italy

# Contents

# Introduction

It is certain that mankind made calculations and considered geometrical figures before the invention of writing. For numbers appeared together with the first writing and soon afterwards there was a highly developed mathematics. In the third millennium BC the Babylonians knew how to solve quadratic equations and were familiar with the theorem now known (quite erroneously) by the name of Pythagoras. What was the purpose of this mathematics? Naturally it was for commercial reckoning, taxation, land surveying, the making of calendars and other quite primitive ends. But from the very beginning mathematics went beyond these requirements. This game of numbers and figures was an end in itself.

In the course of time new fields of application arose. For a long time the most important was astronomy, which also developed in Babylon, in the first millennium BC, and was taken over by the Greeks who put it into a form which remained unchanged for a thousand years.

In this development pure mathematics was always well in advance, both in form and content. The Greeks added much to what they had inherited from the Babylonians. In addition, however, they did something quite new. They made mathematics into a logical system, which starts with certain fundamental assumptions, and proceeds to conclusions via logical deductions, called proofs. This conception of mathematics has remained the standard ever since. Mathematics tells us nothing about reality but states that one thing follows from another in a certain way; anyone can rationally convince himself of the validity of such deductions.

Gradually other sciences made more and more use of

mathematics. The first to do this in a fundamental way was again astronomy. Celestial mechanics needed to use powerful mathematical methods, which to some extent were developed with this application in view.

The possibilities of applying mathematics have expanded continually. Even so, scarcely one per cent of those who learnt mathematics in the secondary schools at the beginning of the century have ever made any use of it.

Why then should they learn mathematics? Mathematics is said to school and sharpen the intellect. This is perhaps claiming too much, but certainly there is something in it. The trained mathematician uses the modes of thought of mathematics at every turn, usually without knowing that he is doing so, or in what way.

What are these modes of thought? There is no short answer to this question, any more than to the question of how to swim. It is, however, possible to demonstrate swimming so that it can be copied. In the same way one can set forth a chain of mathematical thoughts about a subject for the reader to think through and follow. And that is what this book aims to do.

What, then, *is* this mathematics about which the mathematician thinks? This, too, can be shown only by giving examples. In the meantime, however, many activities can be recognised as not being mathematics. Computation is one such activity. Admittedly there was a time when computation was a special skill for the learned, but this time is long since past. Long before the days of calculating machines computation was so organised that it could be done purely mechanically, i.e. without thought. Not even juggling with algebraic formulae is mathematics although, just as in the case of computation, it can be very useful in mathematical thought. Of course the invention of our methods of calculation and our algebra was a mathematical achievement, and even today mathematicians are still occupied with the development of simple methods of calculation, so-called algorithms, in all manner of mathematical fields. Once we have an algorithm, all the rest can be left to a computer. What the computer does is no longer mathematics, but in order to use a computer one needs mathematics and mathematicians.

However, a mathematician must learn the techniques which in practice he would leave to the computer, just as we still have to learn to write with a pen, although the typewriter is faster and more legible. The reader who wishes to learn such techniques should turn to a mathematical textbook where he will find them in a systematic exposition. This, however, is not a textbook. Just as one is shown over a shipyard or a printing press or a school and is led from the drawing office to the slipway, from the composing room to the mailing department or from class to class without wishing to become a shipbuilder, printer or teacher, so in this book the reader is conducted through mathematics, but with no intention of making him a mathematician. He can enter the mathematician's workshop, watch him at work and go away when he has seen enough. He should go into the rooms next door and see what the other mathematicians are doing. It is more difficult to show the connection between the work done in the different rooms, but some feeling for this will surely be picked up.

This book consists of self-contained chapters each treating one theme in a rounded way. Page 100 assumes no knowledge of page 1. The reader can start with the chapter whose title or illustrations attract him most. Although the treatment of individual topics is brief there is no restriction to the superficial or the trivial. The mathematical tourist can be guided to heights or depths without this making him a mountaineer or a pot-holer. Of course not every subject is suited to this treatment. Large parts of mathematics cannot be understood without technical expertise. Mathematicians are well acquainted with this and they also know that things are understood in a more fundamental way if technicalities can be avoided. They are always trying to eliminate the technicalities whenever this is an aid to understanding. Today the layman can be told many more things (and more essential things) about mathematics than fifty years ago. The reader will find a selection of such matters here. He is expected to have retained the essential part of the mathematics he learned at school and, if possible, to have forgotten the inessentials in case they confuse him.

In the course of its development mathematics has expanded not only beyond its own frontiers but also across the boundaries separating the different parts of mathematics. Formerly it was possible to distinguish (with some difficulty) between pure and applied mathematics or between geometry, algebra and analysis; today it is impossible to say when one begins and the other ends. A linguist or a biologist raises a problem and when this has been given a mathematical formulation it lies right in the field of pure mathematics. Geometric problems are solved by algebra and algebraic ones by geometry. From the mechanism of a computer it is a small step to the mechanism of the universe or the mechanism of the thoughts behind our skulls. This book aims to show as much and the reader should not be alarmed if the same chapter treats of coffee mills and distant worlds.

I hope the reader will forgive me if I have occasionally made matters too difficult for him; indeed I hope that he will reckon it to my credit that I have never made them too easy.

# 1 Measuring the world

## Surveying

The first scientist we know by name is Thales of Miletus (sixth century BC). Before him – for two millennia – science was anonymous. Thales is supposed to have predicted an eclipse of the sun – perhaps he had learnt how to do it from Babylonian astronomers. Most of what has been passed on to us of Thales' researches deals with geometry. One of the things attributed to him is that he measured the distance of a ship from the coast. A Roman surveyor tells us how Thales is supposed to have done it.

Let the ship be at A and the coast be along BC (figure 1·1). Let AB be perpendicular to the coast. Let a pole stand at C. Extend BC by its own length, i.e. so that BC = CD. From D, go inland perpendicularly to CD, until you see the pole at C exactly between you and the ship. If this occurs at the point E, you only need to measure DE on land; it is, of course, equal to the required distance.

Thales is also supposed to have been in Egypt and to have surprised the Egyptians there with his measurement of the height of pyramids by means of their shadows – he could have done this similarly.

In the sixth century BC, Eupalinos built an aqueduct on Samos for the tyrant Polycrates. In doing it he had to dig through Mount Castro. The tunnel still exists, over half a mile long, nearly seven feet high and wide. It is excavated from both sides. The error in the middle, where both halves should have met, was ten yards horizontally and ten feet vertically. This error in fact is small – less than 1 %. The Siloah tunnel in

Figure 1·1                    Figure 1·2                         13

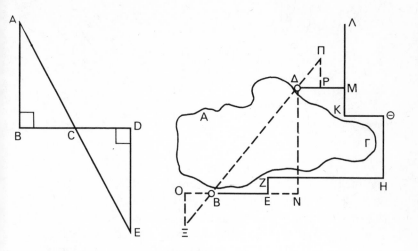

Jerusalem, which was built under King Hiscia in 700 BC, was made far more primitively and inaccurately.

We can read – much later – in Hero how Eupalinos could have done it:

The mountain ΑΒΓΔ (see figure 1·2) should be dug through from B to Δ. Firstly, a broken line ΒΕΖΗΘΚΜΔ whose segments always form right angles is drawn round the mountain. The segments are measured, and so the distances BN and ΔN, which cannot be measured directly, are determined. A triangle BOΞ is now put at B, where BO is a continuation of EB and the angle at O is a right angle, and where OΞ : OB is the known ratio NΔ : BN. Then BΞ gives the direction at B in which one must dig, and it is done similarly at Δ.

A present-day surveyor would work in principle in just the same way. He would not, however, also construct the triangles OBΞ and PΔΠ. For, of course, together with the ratio ΔN : BN, he knows the tangent of the angle ΔNB and,

**Figure 1·3**

**Figure 1·4**

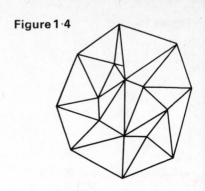

by means of this, from the tangent table, also the angle itself. He is not dependent on geometrical methods, but can reconstruct the unknown angle by calculation. Furthermore, a modern surveyor would not insist on right angles in the arrangement of the joining line segments; with his logarithm table, he has any angle at his disposal with equal ease.

## Triangulation

The determination of distances and angles which cannot be measured directly – that is the surveyor's art. To fix distances by means of the measuring rod or surveyor's chain is a difficult task; to measure angles – with the theodolite – is much easier. If the surveyor has to determine the distance $AB$, which is not directly measurable (figure 1·3), he will measure a segment $AC$ and the angles $ACB$ and $CAB$. If the side $AC$ and the angles at its ends are known, the triangle, and hence the side $AB$, is determined. The actual calculation of $AB$ is done by trigonometrical means,

$$AB : AC = \sin ACB : \sin ABC.$$

$AC$ and $\angle ACB$ are measured directly, $\angle ABC = 180°$ $- \angle BCA - \angle BAC$. $AB$ can now be worked out with the help of the sine table.

Figure 1·5                                                                     15

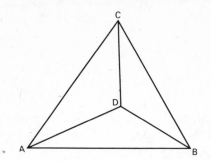

If we want to measure a large area, we cover it with triangles (figure 1·4), in which we measure all kinds of angles; we only need to carry out a measurement of *length* once. We measure many more angles than there are unknowns, e.g. it can happen that we know all three angles of a triangle independently. Their sum must then, of course, be 180°, but mostly this will not be exactly true. The method of apportioning errors is learnt in the calculus of observations which is a branch of general error theory.

A classical task of surveying is the so-called resection: a point $D$ is to be connected to a known triangle by measurement of the angles at $D$ (figure 1·5). The trigonometric formulae, with which this problem is solved, are quite complicated.

## The size of the earth

We have so far behaved as if the earth's surface were a plane. This is how men originally thought of the earth – as a plate swimming in the ocean. Such a view was held by Thales. The spherical shape of the earth must have been discovered in the sixth or fifth centuries BC. The discovery is ascribed to Pythagoras, who is also, though falsely, credited with the theo-

rem on the right-angled triangle; others name Parmenides as
the discoverer, but the younger Democritus seems not yet to
have known anything of the spherical shape of the earth.

The circular shadow of the earth in eclipses of the moon
could have led to the inference of the earth's spherical shape,
and a daily experience at sea also suggested it: when ships
approached from a distance, first their masts and then
gradually their lower parts appeared over the horizon. This
could only be explained by assuming that the earth was a
sphere.

The spherical shape of the earth is most accurately determined *astronomically*. If one is on the earth's surface at a
point $A$, the sky looks different than at, say, the North pole
$N$ (figure 1·6). What is regarded at $A$ as the horizontal plane is
the local tangent plane of the terrestrial globe. It is tilted at an
angle $\varphi$ to the one at the North pole. If $A$ is at latitude 52°,
then $\varphi = 90° - 52° = 38°$. The pole star, which for an
observer at the North pole is in the zenith, has sunk down
through $\varphi$ towards the North for one at $A$ and similarly with
the other heavenly bodies. One can thus read off from the
sky the latitude at which one is. If one goes $\gamma$ degrees to
the South on the same meridian, say from $A$ to $B$ (figure 1·7),
the objects in the northern sky sink through the same number
of degrees; in the southern sky they rise through the same
number of degrees. If the size of $\gamma$ is read in the sky and the
arc $AB$ is measured on earth, the circumference of the earth
can be easily calculated, since

$$\text{Earth's circumference} = AB \cdot 360/\gamma.$$

Indeed, this is quite a simple idea, which the discoverer of

Figure 1·6          Figure 1·7          17

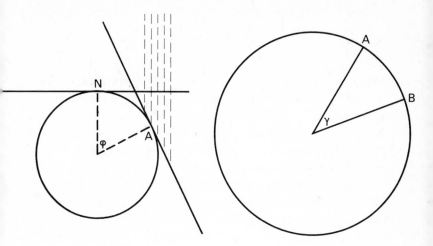

the earth's spherical shape must already have had. The angle in the sky was easy to measure, but distance measurements on earth were not so simple. One certainly knew the distances between ports in terms of number of days' journeys, but what was known about the speed of ships? And how was one to determine whether one town lay due South of another?

A measurement of the earth, which for two millennia remained the standard one, was carried out in the third century BC by the Alexandrian librarian, mathematician, poet, philologist and geographer Eratosthenes. He had been told that Syene, near the first Nile cataracts, lay pretty well exactly south of Alexandria, and that there was a well there into which the sun shone perpendicularly at exactly noon of the longest day. Syene must thus have been on the tropic of Cancer. On the same day at the same hour in Alexandria the sun was a fiftieth of the whole circumference of a circle away from the zenith. This meant that the circumference of the earth is hence obtained, if the distance of Alexandria from

Syene is multiplied by fifty. The story goes that the royal 'pace-counters' measured this distance for Eratosthenes as 5,000 stadia, and the circumference of the earth thus turned out to be 250,000 stadia. We do not know how long Eratosthenes' stadium was. It does not matter anyway, since the assumption that Syene lay south of Alexandria was already imprecise, counting steps is no reliable way of measuring distance, and with the round 5,000 stadia an ample inaccuracy is admitted. One would arrive at the correct circumference of the earth of about 25,000 miles with a stadium of 175 yards, but if the error limits are unknown, such a number does not say very much.

At the beginning of the seventeenth century, the earth was to be measured once again. The Dutchman Willebrord Snell undertook it. Near Leiden, he measured a base line $AB$ of about $\frac{5}{8}$ mile, and he could then lock away his surveyor's chain. He drew imaginary straight lines from the endpoints of the base to Leiden's town hall ($C$) and to the tower of a village church ($D$) and measured the angles at $A$ and $B$. He could thus work out the distance $CD$. At $C$ and $D$ he measured the position of the towers of the nearest towns and villages, and he continued in this way throughout the whole country, to Alkmaar in the north and Bergen op Zoom in the south. Finally, the latitudes of these two places were measured and in the end the earth's circumference appeared as, in modern units, 24,160 miles – an error of 4%. A bad error, since Snell's geodesic measurements were much more accurate; he seems to have worked with a faulty instrument when measuring latitudes.

For two centuries it was the French who, using Snell's principle and with telescopic instruments carried out more and more accurate measurements of the earth and also determined the ellipticity of the earth. When, during the French Revolution, people wanted to put an end to the jumble of weights and measures, it was decided to base them all on a standard metre. This was to be the ten millionth part of the distance between pole and equator; the earth's circumference would then have become exactly 40,000 km. In order to know exactly how long this standard metre was, and to make a specimen, the earth was once again measured. A calibration between Dunkirk and Barcelona was undertaken, lasting six years. Something went wrong with this calibration. One of the collaborators had artificially improved his measurements, and in so doing made them incorrect. When later everything was checked, it appeared that, for various reasons, the metre adopted was too short. The distance between pole and equator, using this metre rule, was not 10,000 km, but 2·3 km longer. The standard rod, which was for over a century taken as the normal metre, lies in a cellar near Paris. Nowadays, however, the metre has been emancipated from this rod; it is now defined in wavelengths of a certain light. Recently it has become possible to determine the shape of the earth much more accurately than with the former geodesic methods. Here, the artificial satellites are important. Their distance from the earth at any time is determined by radar; it is indeed only necessary to see how long it takes from the emission of an electromagnetic wave to the reception of its echo to know how far the satellite is from the observation station at any time. The orbit of the satellite is calculated from these distances. It arises from the force of attraction of the earth and is influenced by the shape of the earth. From the form of the orbit conclusions can be drawn as to the shape of the earth.

## Astronomical distances

Measuring the world – so runs the title of this chapter. The earth is indeed also called 'world', but let us now take a wider meaning of the word. Attempts were made even in antiquity to measure this larger world.

In the third century Aristarchus of Samos, a forerunner of Copernicus as advocate of the heliocentric world picture, wrote a treatise 'On the Size and Distance of Sun and Moon'.

It starts with six assumptions which we give here in modernised form:

1 The moon gets its light from the sun.
2 The earth is at the centre of the moon's orbit.
3 If the moon appears halved, the circle separating light from dark lies in a plane which passes through the eye of the observer.
4 If the moon appears halved, the angle, which the directions from the earth to the sun and moon make, is 87°.
5 The breadth of the earth's shadow is two moons.
6 The breadth of the moon is 2°.

Then Aristarchus' statements follow:

1 The distance from the earth to the sun is in a ratio to the distance from the earth to the moon, which lies between

Figure 1·8 21

18 : 1 and 20 : 1.

2 The same holds for the ratio of the diameters of the sun and moon.

3 The sun's diameter has a ratio to the earth's diameter which lies between 19 : 3 and 43 : 6.

The statements are proved by Aristarchus with all the accuracy of Euclidean geometry.

The first statement follows essentially from the fourth assumption. Imagine the earth at $A$, the moon at $B$, the sun at $C$ (figure 1·8). If the moon is halved, the angle at $B$ is a right angle. The one at $A$ should then be 87°, the one at $C$ is 3°, thus

$$\sin 3° = \frac{AB}{AC},$$

from which this ratio can be calculated, as is given in the first statement (only corrected with regard to the earth's size).

Now Aristarchus uses a fact which he does not mention in the assumptions: that the moon covers the sun just exactly in a total eclipse of the sun. In fact, it follows from this (figure 1·9) that their diameters are in the same ratio as their distances from the earth.

22

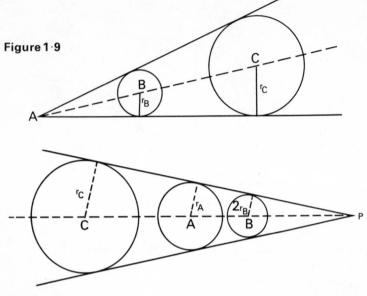

Figure 1·9

Figure 1·10

Assumption 5 concerns the eclipse of the moon (figure 1·10). $A$, $B$, $C$ should again represent the centres of the earth, moon and sun; we call their radii $r_A$, $r_B$, $r_C$. Let the tip of the shadow cone be called $P$. We read off from the figure:

$$CP : AP : BP = r_C : r_A : 2r_B. \qquad (1)$$
$$r_C : r_B = AC : AB$$

has already been worked out. We call this ratio $p$; thus

$$AC : AB = p \qquad (2)$$

and by (1) $\qquad CP : BP = \tfrac{1}{2}p. \qquad (3)$

By (2) $\qquad AC = p \,.\, AB;$

thus $\qquad BC = AC + AB = (p + 1)AB \quad (4)$

By (3) $\qquad CP = \tfrac{1}{2}p \,.\, BP; \qquad (5)$

thus $\qquad BC = CP - BP = (\tfrac{1}{2}p - 1) \,.\, BP \qquad (6)$

Comparing (4) and (6) and putting

$$\frac{p+1}{\frac{1}{2}p-1} = q \tag{7}$$

we get

$$BP = q \cdot AB \tag{8}$$

thus

$$AP = BP + AB = (q+1)AB \tag{9}$$

and by (5) and (8)

$$CP = \tfrac{1}{2}pq \cdot AB \tag{10}$$

Thus by (9) and (10)

$$CP : AP = \tfrac{1}{2}pq : (q+1).$$

This is, on the other hand, precisely the ratio of the radii of the sun and earth, about which Aristarchus' third statement asserts something. If the value found earlier is substituted here for $p$ and the expression (7) is substituted for $q$, Aristarchus' values are obtained.

By the foregoing, since we already know $r_C : r_A$ and $r_C : r_B$, we can also calculate $r_A : r_B$ and, if we use the sixth assumption, $AB : r_B$ (figure 1·11), too, hence $AB : r_A$ as well, i.e. the distance from the earth to the moon, expressed in radii of the earth.

Aristarchus' results are numerically very bad. This is due mainly to the fourth assumption. The angle which is considered there lies very much nearer 90° than Aristarchus thought – he presumably never measured it. The distance

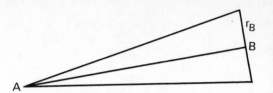

**Figure 1·11**

from the earth to the moon, measured in earth's diameters was quite accurately determined later on in antiquity. The distance from the earth to the sun, and with it also the size of the sun, was, on the other hand, quite considerably underestimated until modern times. The distance of 'near' objects in the universe can nowadays be determined extremely well by means of the radar echo.

With the development of the telescope the determination of distances on Earth and in the universe became more and more reliable. Indeed, the distance of near celestial bodies could be determined by the methods of measurement that were used on the earth. If $A$, $B$ are two points on the earth and $C$ a point of the moon (figure 1·12), one indeed only needs to know the distance $AB$ and the angles at $A$ and $B$ in order to get the distances $AC$ and $BC$ trigonometrically. If $C$ moves far away, $AC$ and $BC$ will in turn become nearly parallel, and finally indistinguishable from parallels. We no longer know how far away they intersect. Very large distances cannot then be distinguished from each other and from infinite distances. Where the boundary lies depends on the quality of the instruments with which the angles at $A$ and $B$ are measured. What matters is the knowledge of $\angle\, ACB = 180° - \angle\, CAB - \angle\, CBA$. If the angles at $A$ and $B$ are approximately right angles, then

$$AC : AB = \sin ABC : \sin ACB,$$

becomes

$$AC = \frac{AB}{\sin ACB} \text{ approximately.}$$

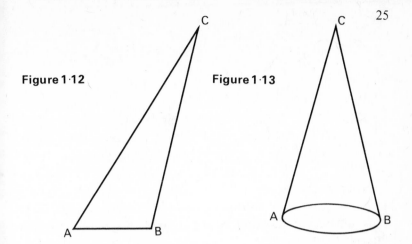

**Figure 1·12**        **Figure 1·13**

If $\measuredangle ACB$ is too small to be measured, we can no longer determine the distance $AC$.

We can of course help ourselves here by enlarging the base line $AB$. But as long as we seek one on the earth, we have no larger base lines at our disposal than the earth's diameter (about 8,000 miles), and in world standards that is a vanishingly small distance. Still, we do not need to abandon the earth in our search for a longer base line. The earth, indeed, travels round the sun and from one end of the earth's orbit to the other is about 180 million miles. We observe the distant point $C$ from two such points of the earth's orbit – not simultaneously, since the journey from one end to the other takes half a year (figure 1·13). We determine the angle at $C$: $\measuredangle ACB = 180° - \measuredangle BAC - \measuredangle ABC$. Half this angle is called the *parallax* of $C$. This is thus the angle which the radius of the earth's orbit would subtend at $C$. The distance from which one must look at the radius of the earth's orbit so that it subtends an angle of one second of arc is called by astronomers a 'parsec'. The full circle has $360 . 60 . 60 = 1296 . 10^3$ seconds of arc; the sine of one second of arc is approximately equal to the corresponding circular arc $= 2\pi/1296 . 10^3$. The radius of the earth's orbit measures approximately $94 . 10^6$ miles. This gives for the parsec $1296 . 10^3 . 94 . 10^6$ miles$/2\pi \sim 19 . 10^{12}$ miles. A parsec is thus nineteen billion miles or, in light years, three and a quarter light years.

The next nearest fixed star to us after the sun is already four light years away. The parallaxes of even the next fixed stars are very small. This caused Copernicus and Galileo much embarrassment. The followers of the geocentric system said, 'If the earth moves around the sun, the fixed stars would have to show parallaxes, but it is known that this is not the case'. The followers of the heliocentric system could of course answer, 'The fixed stars are so far away that their parallaxes are not measurable'. But such a reply looked like an evasion. At first telescopes did not improve matters, and only in the nineteenth century was the first parallax of a fixed star observed. Since then, the determinations of parallax have become more and more refined, but even with the best one hardly gets as far as determining distances of over one hundred light years.

Other methods are used to measure greater distances in the universe. The apparent brightnesses of two objects with the same intrinsic brightness vary inversely as the square of the distances. The distances of two objects can thus be compared by means of their apparent brightnesses, if it is known that they have the same intrinsic brightness. But how can this be determined? There are stars of many classes and types; they differ in colour (more precisely, in their spectrum). Of particular importance are the variable stars which differ, among other things, in their periods. Observations of the 'near' stars have shown that those of the same type have the same intrinsic brightness. If such stars are found farther out, we may assume that they have the same intrinsic brightness and can hence deduce their distance from their apparent brightness. Similarly with the distant galaxies (spiral nebulae), which we may assume are of approximately the same intrinsic brightness. The recession of the galaxies also helps us to measure the universe. The universe is expanding, and because of this the spiral nebulae are receding from us with a velocity which is proportional to their distance from us. The rate of recession can be measured from the shifting of the spectral lines, and this gives values for the spiral nebulae's distances – they probably run into thousands of millions of light years.

## Life on a curved surface

Let us return to Earth. Let us suppose for the moment that there is no astronomy and that the stars are hidden behind permanent clouds. Let us even suppose that the inhabitants of this earth are not allowed to stick their heads into the universe even so far as to discover the curvature of the earth from the gradual appearance of ships over the horizon. Could they even so have discovered the spherical shape of the earth? Of course if anyone goes straight ahead on the

**Figure 1·14**                          **Figure 1·15**

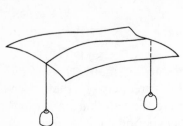

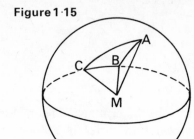

earth he actually describes a great circle of a sphere, i.e. a circle whose plane passes through the centre of the sphere; he finally comes back to his starting point. This could not happen to him on a flat earth. If, now, somebody has travelled a whole lifetime in a straight line and has still not returned to his birthplace, he cannot of course deduce that his earth is a plane. One life may indeed be too short for a world journey. Is it not possible for him, however, to determine whether the earth is flat or curved, and how strong the curvature is, without leaving his own neighbourhood?

Let us suppose he is a geometer. He knows that the sum of the angles of a triangle is equal to two right angles; he knows Pythagoras' theorem. These are theorems of plane geometry. On a sphere or any other curved surface they are not true. To be sure, there are still straight lines in this geometry. What the inhabitant of the sphere calls a straight line – the shortest path joining two points – is called by the observer from outside a great circle; more generally, the shortest lines, which the surface dweller calls *straight*, appear from outside as *curves* (figure 1·14). The surface dweller builds up his triangles with their sides and angles out of such lines. He can measure the triangles. He can test whether plane geometry turns out true, for them.

Suppose he considers the spherical triangle *ABC* (figure

**Figure 1·16**    A    **Figure 1·17**    29

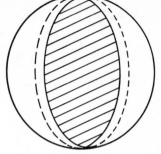

1·15). The angle which he measures there between *his* straight lines *AB* and *AC* (for us, they are circular arcs) is equal to the one between the planes *MAB* and *MAC* (*M* is the sphere's centre). It is in any case larger than the plane angle *BAC*, and the sum of the angles of the surface dweller's triangle *ABC* is larger than that of the plane triangle, i.e. larger than two right angles.

The difference is called the *excess* of the triangle. The larger the triangle is, the larger is its excess. Take on the sphere say *A* as North pole and *B* and *C* 90° apart on the equator (figure 1·16). Such a triangle *ABC* has three right angles, the sum of its angles is 270° and its excess is 90°.

It can be shown that the excess is proportional to the surface area:

What the inhabitant of the sphere calls a straight line is a great circle, i.e. a circle whose plane passes through the centre. Two great circles intersect in diametric points. Together they divide the sphere into four 'lunes' (of which one is hatched in figure 1·17). Let the angle of this lune be $a \cdot 360°$; then its area is $a$ times the surface area of the sphere, i.e.

$$aS,$$

if *S* is the surface area of the sphere.

The triangle *ABC*, bounded by arcs of great circles, lies

30

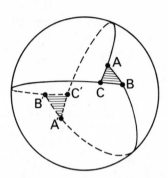

**Figure 1·18**

on the sphere (figure 1·18). We produce the sides, $AB$ beyond $B$, $BC$ beyond $C$, $CA$ beyond $A$, until they intersect again; the arcs passing through $A$ in the antipode $A'$, those through $B$ and $C$ in $B'$ and $C'$ respectively. The surface of the sphere now decomposes into five pieces:

1 The triangle $ABC$,

2 the triangle $A'B'C'$,

3 a lune with vertices $A$, $A'$ and sides passing through $B$ and $C'$,

4 a lune with vertices $B$, $B'$ and sides passing through $C$ and $A'$,

5 a lune with vertices $C$, $C'$ and sides passing through $A$ and $B'$.

Both triangles have the same surface area, which we call $\Delta$. The lunes have the areas $\alpha S$, $\beta S$, $\gamma S$, if $\alpha \cdot 360°$, $\beta \cdot 360°$, $\gamma \cdot 360°$ are the exterior angles of the triangle $ABC$. They must all add up to $S$. Thus

$$2\Delta + (\alpha + \beta + \gamma)S = S.$$

If we work with the interior angles $\alpha'\,.\,360°$, $\beta'\,.\,360°$, $\gamma'\,.\,360°$ of the triangle, we have $\alpha'\,.\,360° + \alpha\,.\,360° = 180°$, etc. Thus $\alpha = \frac{1}{2} - \alpha'$, $\beta = \frac{1}{2} - \beta'$, $\gamma = \frac{1}{2} - \gamma'$. Substituting these we get

$$2\Delta + (\tfrac{3}{2} - \alpha' - \beta' - \gamma')S = S,$$

i.e.
$$\alpha' + \beta' + \gamma' - \tfrac{1}{2} = \frac{2\Delta}{S}.$$

The excess of the triangle is

$$(\alpha' + \beta' + \gamma')\,.\,360° - 180° = (\alpha' + \beta' + \gamma' - \tfrac{1}{2})360° =$$
$$= \frac{2\Delta}{S}\,.\,360° \qquad (1)$$

The excess of a triangle with three right angles, which fills an eighth of the sphere, indeed turns out to be 90°.

Let us now put ourselves in the place of a sphere dweller ignorant of the curvature of his world. He measures small triangles, and at first he does not notice anything. He measures larger triangles, and it appears that the sum of their angles is larger than 180°. First he thinks there has been an error in measurement. But the deviations repeat and increase with the size of the triangles. How is he to explain that to himself? A systematic investigation shows that the excess of the triangles is proportional to their area. And now the illuminating idea occurs to him that he lives on a sphere. Indeed, he can even calculate the total area of the sphere: if it is $S$, and if $\Delta$ is the area of a triangle with excess $\varepsilon$, he gets

$$S = \frac{2\Delta\,.\,360°}{\varepsilon}.$$

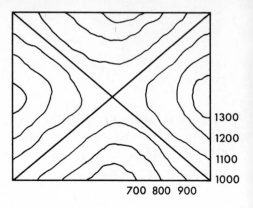

1300
1200
1100
1000

700 800 900

**Figure 1·19**

From the area of the sphere he also knows its radius $r$, since

$$S = 4\pi r^2$$

$$K = \frac{1}{r^2}$$

is called the curvature of the sphere – the smaller the radius is the more strongly the sphere is curved. In terms of the sphere dweller's data, the curvature $K$ of his world is expressed as

$$K = \frac{2\pi}{\Delta} \cdot \frac{\varepsilon}{360°}.$$

He can determine the curvature of his world from the measured $\Delta$ and $\varepsilon$.

This holds also if the world is not exactly a sphere, but is irregularly curved. The ratio of excess and area of a triangle will not then be the same everywhere in his world; it will vary from place to place with the curvature of the world. But it is also then a measure of the local curvature at each point.

Actually, the curvature thus defined can be negative as well. We talk of negative curvature, if the sum of the triangle's angles is less than 180°, i.e. if it shows a *defect* or negative excess. This can in fact happen. Imagine the surface of a mountain range and in the range a pass. A map with con-

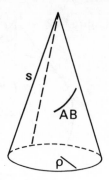

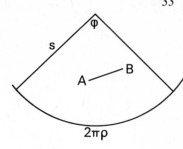

Figure 1·20a        Figure 1·20b

tour lines looks something like figure 1·19 in the neighbourhood of the pass; the pass is at a height of one thousand feet;
the terrain rises to East and West, falls to North and South,
and the pass runs from North to South. Near a pass triangles
have a defect (we do not prove this here); the curvature of
the surface is negative there.

The theorem on the sum of the angles is naturally not the
only one which is violated in curved worlds. If we return to
the sphere, we see that Pythagoras' theorem is not true there
either. A triangle with three right angles is equilateral there;
we get $c^2 < a^2 + b^2$ instead of the usual equality of Pythagoras. The sphere dweller can also calculate the curvature
of this world from the defect in Pythagoras' theorem.

We shall deal with one more deviation from plane geometry which the inhabitant of the spherical world notices.
First, however, we deal with a conical world.

If we cut open the cone of figure 1·20 along the dotted
generator, we can flatten out the cone's surface on the plane.
The result is the circular sector next to it with angle $\varphi$. In this
the arc $2\pi\rho$ of the sector has the same ratio to the whole
circumference $2\pi s$ as $\varphi$ has to 360°,

$$\varphi = \frac{\rho}{s}.\ 360°.$$

Figure 1·21

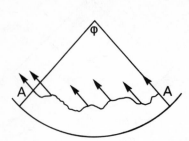

Figure 1·22

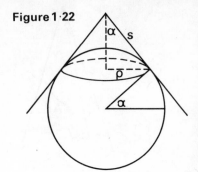

Nothing is stretched or shortened in the flattening out. All distances remain unchanged, the whole geometry remains unchanged; what turns out to be a straight line in the flattening out, is also called a straight line by the cone dweller. One would think that exactly the same geometry holds on the cone as on the plane, but this is not quite true. As long as he does not make any long journeys, the cone dweller does not notice that he is not sitting in a plane. Of course, at the vertex of the cone he would notice something odd, but let us suppose for the moment that this singular point is inaccessible to him! We now let the cone dweller undertake a journey around his world, and let him move an arrow, which is lying on the surface, parallel to itself. Let us say that at the start of the journey at $A$ (figure 1·21) the arrow pointed along the generator; when the traveller again comes to $A$ (on the left) the arrow makes an angle $\varphi$ with the same generator. The world traveller discovers that a direction which he took with him experienced a change of $\varphi$. On short journeys this does not happen; for this sort of thing to occur, one must sail round the vertex of the cone; if it is circumnavigated several times on the journey, the direction must alter by the same multiple of $\varphi$.

This is how it appears from the outside. The arrow has experienced a rotation $\varphi = \rho/s \cdot 360°$. The cone traveller sees it somewhat differently. Seen from the outside, he has turned through 360°. Seen from his point of view, the arrow's rotation amounts to $360° - \varphi = (1 - \rho/s). \, 360°$.

We leave the conical world and return to the spherical world. The sphere dweller should make a journey round the North pole on a circle of latitude. At the same time he should take an arrow with him and move it parallel to itself in the sense of his geometry. How does he do this? We imagine the tangent cone attached to his circle of latitude (figure 1·22). Now, when the sphere dweller travels on the circle of latitude, he has only to deal with the nearest neighbourhood of this circle; in moving the arrow he is not at all concerned with the behaviour of the surface further away. He will thus behave exactly as the cone dweller, i.e. like an inhabitant of the tangent cone. He will return home with a deviation of the arrow.

How large is this deviation? We have worked this out before:

$$\left(1 - \frac{\rho}{s}\right). \; 360°,$$

where $\rho$ is the radius and $s$ is the generator of the cone. We express this in the sphere's data, $\rho/s$ is the sine of the angle denoted by $a$ in figure 1·22, which is also called the latitude of the circle of latitude. After a round trip at latitude $a$, the arrow's deviation is

$$(1 - \sin a) . 360°.$$

As a check: at latitude 90° the effect vanishes. Seen from outside, the traveller rotates once, taking the arrow with

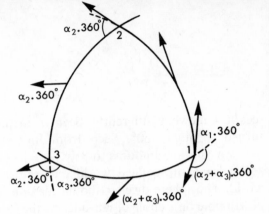

**Figure 1·23**

him: the arrow is thus rotated through 360°. But with respect to the traveller nothing has happened to the arrow.

The traveller on the circle of latitude journeys round a cap of the sphere. The area of the sphere's cap which is above latitude $a$ is

$$(1 - \sin a) . 2\pi r^2,$$

if $r$ is the radius of the sphere – we take this formula as known. Let us now calculate angles in radians and thus say $2\pi$ instead of 360°. Hence

rotation of arrow divided by circumscribed area = curvature ($= 1/r^2$).

We test this result in another example:

For the sphere dweller, a parallel of latitude is not straight. His straight lines are what we call great circles. We now let him travel round a triangle, i.e. straight from 1 to 2, then from 2 to 3 and finally from 3 to 1. So long as he travels straight, the arrow's direction makes the same angle with the direction of travel (see figure 1·23). Let us say that on departure at 1 the arrow's direction concides with the direction of travel. Then it stays like this on the way from 1 to 2. At 2 the traveller changes his direction by the exterior angle $a_2 . 360°$. The arrow of course is not allowed to turn with him. It now makes the angle $-a_2 . 360°$ with the direction of travel. It stays like this until arrival at 3. There the direction of travel again changes, now by the exterior angle $a_3 . 360°$. The arrow now makes the angle $(-a_2 - a_3) . 360°$ with the direction of travel. It stays like this for a while, namely until return to 1. If the traveller again puts himself in the direction he started in, he turns through the exterior angle $a_1 . 360°$. The arrow now makes an angle $(-a_1 - a_2 - a_3) . 360°$ with the direction of departure, i.e. with its original position. For the same reasons as before, we add $360°$ and say $2\pi$ radians instead of $360°$. Then we get that the rotation of the arrow after one circuit round the triangle is

$$(1 - a_1 - a_2 - a_3) . 2\pi.$$

By formula (1) this is equal to

$$\frac{2\Delta}{S} . 2\pi,$$

where $\Delta$ is the area of the triangle and $S$ is the surface area of the sphere, i.e.

$$S = 4\pi r^2.$$

If we now divide the arrow's rotation by the area of the triangle, we again get $1/r^2$, i.e. the curvature of the sphere.

The sphere dweller, and in fact the dweller of any curved world, can determine *how* curved it is by observing the arrow's rotation on a round trip and dividing it by the enclosed area. He thereby gets the curvature, which, besides, can vary from place to place.

To translate an arrow keeping its direction fixed one can for example make use of a spinning top with horizontal axis (gyroscope); from mechanics we know that such an instrument maintains the direction of its axis. A pendulum can also be used; it does not alter its direction of swing. Naturally, under transport on a surface curved in space there will have to be some change, after all; the axis of the gyroscope or the direction of swing of the pendulum lies in the tangent plane, and the position of the tangent plane in space of course must alter at each moment of the journey. The changes in the axis of the gyroscope or the direction of swing occur perpendicularly to the tangent plane at each instant; their tangential components remain the same. This way of moving an arrow on a curved surface, which we have just considered, is named after the Italian mathematician T. Levi – Civita (1917), who developed it. It has really been known for a quite long time, however.

In the spring of 1851 there was a sensation in Paris. It was shown there to all who did not yet believe it that the earth rotates about its axis. The physicist Foucault had caused a pendulum 220 ft long with a weight of 61 lb to be hung in the Panthéon. It traced out its swing in a pile of sand on the floor, and everybody could see how, after several minutes, it had altered its direction. One saw, so to speak, how the earth rotated under the pendulum. At the North pole, the direction of swing would have to run through all the points of the compass once in exactly 24 hours, in the opposite direction to the earth's rotation. At lower latitudes it is less – we shall return to this directly.

It was the first really obvious proof of the earth's rotation. All the other effects, with which people had experimented earlier, were so insignificant that they could only be shown by precision measurements and could not be used for public demonstration. Foucault's experiment was immediately copied throughout the world. In the Musée des Arts et Métiers in Paris a Foucault pendulum can be seen hanging and swinging, as also in the palace of the United Nations in New York or the Science Museum in London.

What has the Foucault pendulum to do with the geometry of curved surfaces? Now, the rotating globe carries us and the Foucault pendulum once every 24 hours round a circle of latitude of a globe which may be thought of as fixed in space. We have indeed already worked out how much the direction of the arrow, which is taken along, will have rotated after the journey: it is $(1 - \sin a) \cdot 360°$, if $a$ is the latitude of the circle of latitude. Anyway, we must, since we have to consider the rotating instead of the fixed earth, subtract the real rotation from $360°$. The deviation of the Foucault pendulum after 24 hours is thus

$$\sin a \cdot 360°.$$

In our latitudes, the direction of swing moves about three times more slowly than the hour hand (which describes the clock-face *twice* in 24 hours). This movement can be seen, if only the hand is long enough; in Foucault's experiment, the amplitude of the huge pendulum corresponds to the length of the watch hand.

## The curvature of space

We saw how the inhabitant of a curved world finds out, from measurements inside this world and without leaving it, how strongly his world is curved. In this connection, we thought of a surface as the world and of an inhabitant restricted to this surface world. To a certain extent, this is the situation of Man on Earth. He projects enough above the earth's surface, however, to have discovered its spherical shape with his own eyes before he could establish it by measurement. Furthermore, his sight teaches him that there is more to the world than the surface on which he moves.

We saw earlier how man measures the three-dimensional world. Not with ruler and measuring tape, for they are not enough even on earth. If a surveyor wishes to bring three points into a straight line, he takes bearings. The straight lines which he draws are light rays, and these are also the straight lines of the astronomer in the universe.

Now the surveyor indeed knows that the linearity of light rays should preferably not be assumed through thick and thin. If a rudder appears broken through the water, it is more sensible to assume that something happens to the light rays when they pass from water into air than to maintain that the light ray is still straight, but the rudder is broken. The surveyor corrects for the refraction of light rays before he accepts them as straight lines. The astronomer does the same thing with his measurements in the universe. Owing to refraction in the atmosphere, sun beams become bent and the sun is seen a short time after it should have set. The astronomer has more to correct for near the horizon than high in the sky.

However, there are still other causes of the bending of light rays. Gravity, for example. Those light rays coming from a star which nearly graze the sun are bent like the path of a comet. Seen from the earth, such a star appears to have moved slightly away from the sun – something which had been predicted by Einstein and was confirmed by observations of solar eclipses.

One can form triangles in the universe with – possibly corrected – light rays as straight lines. In 'small' triangles (say of the size of the solar system), no deviation of the sum of the angle from 180° can be detected; interstellar space still seems flat in such dimensions. However, any excess or defect increases with the size of the triangles, and triangles the size of the universe could well exhibit a measurable excess or defect. The universe would be curved. There are indirect arguments for assuming that this is indeed the case. According to these the radius of curvature of the universe would be several thousands of millions of light years.

It can be shown mathematically that such a positively curved universe must be finite and closed; a closed space, just as the surface of a sphere is a closed surface. If we travel straight on through such a world, we return to our starting point, as on earth.

How are we to imagine this? A closed surface can be placed in space and considered from all sides. But a closed space?

If an inhabitant of a spherical surface, who cannot imagine a globe, wants to draw a picture of his world, how does he do it? He draws himself two maps, one of the eastern hemisphere and one of the western hemisphere, and puts them side by side. In fact such a pair of maps for the earth can be found in every atlas; from the degrees of longitude on the edge, from the equator and from other idenfication marks, it can be seen how the edges will have to be identified.

We can treat the closed universe similarly. We dissect the universe along a spherical surface. It is split into two parts: solid spheres, filled with stars and galaxies. We make a model of each of the halves and place them in front of us on the writing desk, two transparent globes, in which particles of dust indicate the spiral nebulae. The spherical surface, along which we have cut the universe, is twice visible in our models: as the surfaces of the two globes. We have only to attach identification marks to it that say which point of one coincides with which point of the other.

Such a universe is indeed closed. Each journey straight onwards is a round trip. It does not matter if at any time we leave one of the spheres in the model, since we then simultaneously enter the other model sphere. Just as much or as little occurs here as if, on a terrestrial journey the equator or null meridian is crossed. The intersecting surface is not a boundary; it only seems so in the model.

There is another thing about the curved universe in which the astronomers have placed us: it is swelling out. The distances in the universe are increasing, the spiral nebulae are fleeing from us and from each other. Thousands of millions of years ago this process is thought to have started with a closely packed universe.

But all this belongs already to astronomy and no longer to geometry.

# 2 Ad infinitum

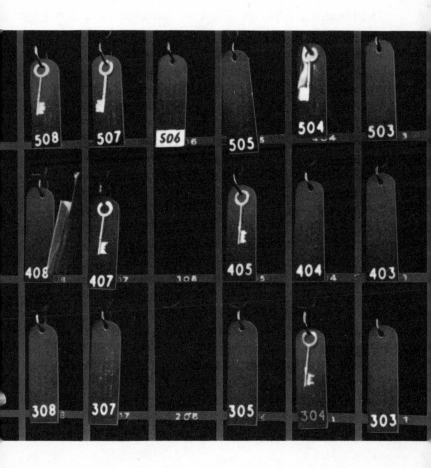

## Counting

A hotel has infinitely many rooms which are numbered

$$1, 2, 3, \ldots ,$$

The hotel is completely full. Late one evening, a new guest arrives. Full, says the porter. Never mind, says the manager, the guest in no. 1 moves into no. 2, the one in no. 2 into no. 3, the one in no. 3 into no. 4 and so on, and the new guest can move into the free room 1.

But, much later another 1,000 new guests arrive. Full, says the porter. Never mind, says the manager, the guest in no. 1 moves into no. 1,001, the one in no. 2 into 1,002 and so on, and the new guests can move into the free rooms 1 to 1,000.

And suddenly a further infinite number of guests appear, Messrs. $A_1$, $A_2$, $A_3$, .... Full, says the porter. Never mind, says the manager, we let the guest in no. 1 move to no. 2, the one in no. 2 to no. 4, the one in no. 3 to no. 6, each one to the room with twice the number, and then $A_1$, $A_2$, $A_3$, ... can be accommodated in rooms 1, 3, 5, ....

This pretty story is due to the great mathematician David Hilbert (1862–1943). In it he considers ideas which stem already from Georg Cantor (1845–1918).

The series of natural numbers

$$1, 2, 3, \ldots$$

is infinite. It can be continued as far as desired. The series of even numbers

$$2, 4, 6, \ldots$$

is also infinite. The even numbers are only a part of all

natural numbers. Yet their infinity is not smaller than that of all integers. They can indeed be so arranged,

$$1, 2, 3, 4, 5, \ldots,$$
$$2, 4, 6, 8, 10, \ldots,$$

that exactly one even number corresponds to each natural number and vice versa. The guests of the full hotel can also be accommodated in the even-numbered rooms.

If I write

| 1 | 2 | 3 | 4 | $\ldots,$ |
|------|------|------|------|------|
| 1000 | 2000 | 3000 | 4000 | $\ldots,$ |

it is seen that the numbers divisible by 1000 still have the same infinity. Similarly with the numbers from 1001 onwards:

| 1 | 2 | 3 | 4 | $\ldots,$ |
|------|------|------|------|------|
| 1001 | 1002 | 1003 | 1004 | $\ldots.$ |

What about the positive, rational numbers (i.e. fractions like $\frac{7}{3}$, $\frac{2}{5}$ etc.)? I write them down consecutively under the natural numbers:

| 1 | 2 | 3 | 4 | 5 | 6 | 7 | 8 | 9 | 10 | 11 | $\ldots$ |
|---|---|---|---|---|---|---|---|---|----|----|---|
| $\frac{1}{1}$ | $\frac{1}{2}$ | $\frac{2}{1}$ | $\frac{1}{3}$ | $\frac{3}{1}$ | $\frac{1}{4}$ | $\frac{2}{3}$ | $\frac{3}{2}$ | $\frac{4}{1}$ | $\frac{1}{5}$ | $\frac{5}{1}$ | $\ldots$ |

This arrangement is quite systematic: first, all numbers $\frac{a}{b}$ with $a + b = 2$, then with $a + b = 3$, then with $a + b = 4$, etc. and for fixed $n$ we arrange the numbers $\frac{a}{b}$ with $a + b = n$ according to $a$'s size; in doing this we omit fractions which can be cancelled.

The infinity of the rational numbers is thus not larger than that of the integers.

An infinite set $M$ of objects is called *countably* infinite, if it can be put into correspondence with the set of natural numbers in such a way that exactly one object of $M$ corresponds to each natural number, and vice versa. In other words, a set is countably infinite, if it can be accommodated in the hotel with rooms 1, 2, 3, ... , so that each room is occupied by one object.

All the infinite sets which we have discussed up to now are countably infinite. Are there also others? The answer is yes.

Consider a line-segment $A$. It has infinitely many points. I claim that the set of its points is not countably infinite.

Would anyone like to claim that it is in fact countably infinite? He has then to enumerate all the points of $A$ as a sequence

$$a_1, a_2, a_3, \ldots ,$$

from which no point of $A$ may be missing. I shall show that he has still forgotten one point.

He thus begins to enumerate the points of $A$, and while he is busy with this, I shall construct a point which he must forget.

He says $a_1$. Then I choose a subsegment $A_1$ of $A$ which does not contain the point $a_1$. (In figure 2·1, I have drawn it below, but in reality it lies on $A$.) My opponent now says $a_2$. I choose a subsegment $A_2$ of $A_1$ which does not contain $a_2$ (drawn above $A$ instead of on $A$). My opponent says $a_3$, and I choose a subsegment $A_3$ which does not contain $a_3$. We continue in this way. At each stage

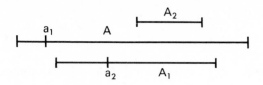

**Figure 2·1**

47

$A_{n+1}$ is a subsegment of $A_n$,

and

$a_n$ is not on $A_n$.

I further make sure that at each stage the segment $A_{n+1}$ is at most half as long as $A_n$. The segments $A_n$ finally collapse on to a point $c$. This point $c$, I claim, has been necessarily forgotten by my opponent.

Indeed, can $c = a_1$? No, since $c$ is on $A_1$, while $A_1$ was precisely chosen so that it does not contain $a_1$. Can $c = a_2$? No, since $c$ is on $A_2$, while $A_2$ should precisely not contain $a_2$. It goes on in this way. Can $c = a_{1000}$? It cannot either, for $c$ is on $A_{1000}$, where $a_{1000}$ certainly does not lie. In general, $c$ cannot coincide with any of the points $a_1, a_2, \ldots$, which my opponent has enumerated. My opponent has not enumerated the whole of $A$; he has forgotten $c$.

I should have started with $c$, he says (like the man who had wagered that he would eat twenty potato dumplings, got to the nineteenth and then looked sadly at the twentieth: if only I had started with you). But, of course, if he had started with $c$, I would have produced another missing point for him. However he enumerates a countably infinite set of points of $A$, he will not exhaust $A$.

The set of points of a line-segment is no longer countably infinite. It is of a larger infinity.

This theorem stems from Georg Cantor, too. Cantor also brought up the question of whether there is another infinity between countable infinity and that of the line-segment. Cantor toiled in vain to solve this problem, and others after him have come to grief over it. After these unsuccessful efforts more critical people examined how in fact one had to formulate this problem exactly, and in 1963 P.J.Cohen proved that it is insoluble. More precisely, one can just as well answer it by yes as by no, without striking a contradiction. With that the matter need not be finished, however. Perhaps we have not formulated the problem 'correctly' yet.

## Natural numbers

Let us return to the natural numbers. All sorts of things can be done with them. For example, they can be added.

$$a + b = b + a,$$

the so-called commutative law, is familiar. But is it also true? and what about

$$(a + b) + c = a + (b + c),$$

the so-called associative law? Can this sort of thing be proved? Are there not infinitely many assertions in one formula? How can infinitely many assertions be proved?

Before one goes into this question, one must first of all determine what $a + b$ means. Yes of course, again a natural number, but which one? I must first of all define an infinite number of objects. How am I to define infinitely many objects?

The series of the natural numbers starts with 1. In it, each object has exactly one successor and each, except for 1, has also exactly one predecessor. The successor of $n$ we call $n'$.

> *Definition* of $a + b$:
> for $b = 1 : a + b = a'$
> for $b = n' : a + b = (a + n)'$.

This means: $a + 1$ is the successor of $a$, and if I already know what $a + n$ is, I put $a +$ successor of $n =$ successor of $a + n$.

In other words

$$(K_1) \qquad a + (n + 1) = (a + n) + 1.$$

This is already the associative law for $n$ in place of $b$ and 1 in place of $c$.

*Proof* of

$$(K_c) \qquad a + (b + c) = (a + b) + c:$$

The assertion is, by $(K_1)$, true for $c = 1$. I assume it is true for $c = n$ and any $a$, $b$, i.e.

$$(K_n) \qquad a + (b + n) = (a + b) + n,$$

and I obtain from $(K_n)$ the formula

$$(K_{n'}) \qquad a + (b + n') = (a + b) + n'.$$

This is done as follows:

$$
\begin{aligned}
a + (b + n') &= a + (b + (n + 1)) && \text{by definition,} \\
&= a + ((b + n) + 1) && \text{by } K_1 \text{ for } b \text{ instead of } a, \\
&= (a + (b + n)) + 1 && \text{by } K_1 \text{ for } b+n \text{ instead} \\
& && \text{of } n, \\
&= ((a + b) + n) + 1 && \text{by } K_n,
\end{aligned}
$$

$$= (a + b) + (n + 1) \quad \text{by } K_1 \text{ for } a+b \text{ instead of } a,$$
$$= (a + b) + n' \qquad \text{by definition.}$$

To sum up: we started with $K_1$. We showed that if $K_n$ is true, then so is $K_{n'}$ ($n'$ is the successor of $n$). From this it follows that $K_c$ is true for every $c$ and thus

$$(K_c) \qquad a + (b + c) = (a + b) + c$$

is proved.

The method of proof which we have used here is called proof by induction or inference from $n$ to $n + 1$. We know that $K_1$ is true. We show that, under the assumption $K_n$, $K_{n+1}$ is true, too. We then have that $K_n$ holds for every subscript. Of course, $K_2$ then follows from $K_1$, $K_3$ follows from $K_2$, etc., ad infinitum.

This is expressed in a general way as the

> *Principle of Complete Induction*:
> Let $E_1$ be true;
> whenever $E_n$ is true, let $E_{n+1}$ be true also.
> Then $E_n$ holds in general.

Using this principle, we now carry out the *proof* of

$$(L_a) \qquad a + 1 = 1 + a:$$

Trivially, $L_1$ is true. Let

$$(L_n) \qquad n + 1 = 1 + n$$

be true. Then

$$(n + 1) + 1 = (1 + n) + 1 \qquad \text{by } L_n$$
$$= 1 + (n + 1) \qquad \text{by } K_1,$$

i.e. $L_{n+1}$ is true. In other words, $L_1$ is true, and if $L_n$ is true, so is $L_{n+1}$. Thus $L_a$ holds in general.

   *Proof* of

   $(M_b)$      $a + b = b + a$:

$M_1$ is the same as $L_a$, which we have just proved. Let $M_n$ be true for arbitrary $a$, i.e.

   $(M_n)$      $a + n = n + a$.

Then

$$a + (n + 1) = (a + n) + 1 = (n + a) + 1 =$$
$$= 1 + (n + a) = (1 + n) + a = (n + 1) + a.$$

Thus, $M_1$ is true, and if $M_n$ is true, so is $M_{n+1}$. Thus $M_b$ is true for all $b$.

We can also define the multiplication of natural numbers now.

   *Definition*:
   $$a \cdot 1 = a$$
   $$a(n + 1) = an + a.$$

By the principle of complete induction it can be seen that $ab$ is then defined generally.

We prove a few more rules of reckoning for products:

   *Proof* of

   $(N_c)$      $(a + b)c = ac + bc$:

$N_1$ is correct, since $a \cdot 1 = a$, $b \cdot 1 = b$. Let

   $(N_n)$      $(a + b)n = an + bn$

be true. Then

$$(a + b) \cdot (n + 1) = (a + b) \cdot n + (a + b)$$
$$\text{(definition of product)}$$
$$= (a \cdot n + b \cdot n) + (a + b)$$

which, by repeated application of the commutative and associative laws, gives

$$(a \cdot n + a) + (b \cdot n + b).$$

By the definition of product, this is

$$a \cdot (n + 1) + b \cdot (n + 1),$$

by means of which $N_{n+1}$ is deduced from $N_n$. $N_c$ has thus been shown to be true in general.

> *Proof* of
> $(P_a)$     $1 \cdot a = a$:

$P_1$ follows from the definition of product.

> $(P_n)$     $1 \cdot n = n$

implies     $1 \cdot (n + 1) = 1 \cdot n + 1 = n + 1,$

i.e. $P_{n+1}$, and thus $P_a$ is proved in general.

> *Proof* of
> $(Q_b)$     $a \cdot b = b \cdot a$:

$Q_1$ is the same as $P_a$.

> $(Q_n)$     $a \cdot n = n \cdot a$

implies     $a \cdot (n + 1) = a \cdot n + a = n \cdot a + a = n \cdot a + 1 \cdot a,$

and by $N_a$ for $n$ instead of $a$ and 1 instead of $b$ this is

$$(n + 1) \cdot a,$$

and thus $Q_{n+1}$ is deduced from $Q_n$. This has proved $Q_b$.

This was our answer to the question: how can infinitely many assertions be proved? It is done by complete induction.

Complete induction can also be used to define an infinite sequence of objects. To define $a^n$ one puts

$$a^1 = a \text{ and } a^{n+1} = a^n \cdot a.$$

Then $a^n$ is defined for all $n = 1, 2, \ldots$ .

We have already defined addition in a like manner:

$$a + 1 = a' \, , \, a + n' = (a + n)' \, .$$

We prescribed rules for addition and deduced further rules from these.

We have not investigated whether the prescribed rules are satisfactory. By that I mean whether $a + b$ and $ab$ are uniquely defined for all $a$ and $b$ in consequence of the rules. To show this would be more involved than the preceding discussion and I shall not bore the reader with it.

## Prime numbers

In the series of the natural numbers,

$$2, 3, 5, 7, 11, 13, 17, 19, 23, 29, 31, \ldots$$

are called prime numbers, because they cannot be written as the product of other numbers.

$$4 = 2.2, \, 6 = 2.3, \, 8 = 2.2.2, \, 9 = 3.3, \ldots$$

are not prime numbers. If $n$ is not a prime number, it can be decomposed into factors, and continuing in this way, we can write $n$ as a product of prime numbers. The number 1 is not counted as a prime number.

How many prime numbers are there? Does the series of prime numbers ever stop?

Let us suppose that it stops. There are thus only a finite number of prime numbers

$$p_1, p_2, \ldots, p_k.$$

We form the product of these numbers plus 1, i.e.

$$P = p_1 p_2 \ldots p_k + 1.$$

This is bigger than each of the numbers $p_1$, $p_2$, $\ldots$, $p_k$. Since these already should be all the prime numbers, $P$ cannot be a prime number, and it can thus be written as a product of prime numbers. In any case, there is a prime number contained in $P$. But $p_1$, $p_2$, $\ldots$, $p_k$ are *all* the prime numbers. $P$ must thus be divisible by one of the numbers $p_1$, $p_2$, $\ldots$, $p_k$. But this is impossible, since if I divide $P$ by one of the numbers $p_1$, $p_2$, $\ldots$, $p_k$, I get the remainder 1. Thus my assumption that I can exhaust the prime numbers by a finite enumeration is false. Hence,

*there are infinitely many prime numbers.*

This theorem is already stated by Euclid (fourth century BC).

I consider the numbers of the form $4n - 1$, i.e.

$$3, 7, 11, 15, 19, 23, 27, 31, \ldots .$$

Are there also infinitely many prime numbers among these?

The numbers of the form $4n - 1$ are odd. The other odd numbers are of the form $4n - 3$. If I multiply two numbers of this latter form together, say $4n - 3$ by $4m - 3$, I get

$(4n - 3)(4m - 3) = 4(4nm - 3n - 3m + 3) - 3$, i.e. one of the same kind. A number of the form $4n - 1$ thus cannot be composed only of numbers of the form $4n - 3$. If I decompose a number of the form $4n - 1$ into prime factors, at least one number of the same form must occur there. A number of the form $4n - 1$ thus has a prime divisor of the same form.

If I multiply two numbers of the first form together, say $4n - 1$ by $4m - 1$, I get $(4n - 1)(4m - 1) = 4(4nm - n - m + 1) - 3$, i.e. one of the second kind. A product with an even number of factors of the form $4n - 1$ is thus of the form $4n - 3$; if I add 2, I get a number of the original form.

Let us suppose that there are only a finite number of prime numbers of the form $4n - 1$, say

$$p_1, p_2, \ldots, p_k.$$

I should like $k$ to be even and therefore, if it should be necessary, write 3 down twice; i.e. $p_1 = p_2 = 3, p_3 = 7$, etc.

$$P = p_1 p_2 \ldots p_k + 2$$

is, as we saw, again of the form $4n - 1$. It cannot be a prime number, because it is larger than all the prime numbers $p_1, \ldots, p_k$. Since $P$ is of the form $4n - 1$, it must have a prime factor of the form $4n - 1$, and this must occur among $p_1, \ldots, p_k$. This is impossible, however, because division of $P$ by each of the $p_1, \ldots, p_k$ leaves the remainder 2. The hypothesis was thus false. Hence

*there are infinitely many prime numbers of the form* 4n − 1.

There are also infinitely many prime numbers of the form $4n - 3$, but that is much harder to prove.

More generally, among the numbers

$$a, a + d, a + 2d, a + 3d, \ldots$$

there are infinitely many prime numbers, provided $a$ and $d$ do not have a common divisor $\neq 1$.

That is a theorem which is very difficult to prove.

## Rational and irrational numbers

A line-segment can be doubled, trebled, etc. and also halved, divided into three, etc. Starting with the unit segment, we obtain segments of length $\frac{m}{n}$ in this way, where $m$ and $n$ are natural numbers. These correspond to the positive, rational numbers, which, as we know, form a countably infinite set. The points of a segment, however, form a set of larger infinity. Thus there are certainly segments whose length is irrational.

Such segments can be easily quoted. The diagonal of a square of side 1 has length $\sqrt{2}$, as is deduced from Pythagoras' theorem. $\sqrt{2}$ is not rational. Indeed, if

(*) $$\sqrt{2} = \frac{p}{q}$$

with natural numbers $p$, $q$ which can be taken as having no common divisor, squaring would give

$$2 = \frac{p^2}{q^2},$$

i.e.
$$2q^2 = p^2,$$

thus $p^2$ and hence also $p$ would have to be even,

$$p = 2p'$$

with $p'$ a natural number. Hence

$$2q^2 = 4p'^2,$$
$$q^2 = 2p'^2,$$

thus $q^2$ and hence also $q$ would be even, and then $p$ and $q$ would both be even and thus have a common divisor. The assumption was thus impossible.

$$\sqrt{2} \text{ is irrational.}$$

But how long is the diagonal in actual fact?

$\sqrt{2}$ is by definition the positive solution of the equation

$$x^2 = 2.$$

This equation cannot be solved exactly by rational numbers, but can it perhaps approximately? Indeed it can, and if we are clever we can find very good approximations very quickly.

We must find a square with the area 2. Instead of this we can look at square-like rectangles the sides of which hardly differ. Try, for instance

Take

$$a_1 = 1$$

as one side. Then the other must be

$$b_1 = 2.$$

This is a bad approximation; the sides differ considerably.

We now average and set

$$a_2 = \frac{1}{2}(a_1 + b_1) = \frac{3}{2},$$

$$b_2 = \frac{2}{a_2} = \frac{4}{3}.$$

The rectangle with sides $\frac{2}{3}$ and $\frac{4}{3}$ has area 2, and it already looks more similar to a square. We continue in this way. We again average:=

$$a_3 = \frac{1}{2}(a_2 + b_2) = \frac{17}{12},$$

$$b_3 = \frac{2}{a_3} = \frac{24}{17}.$$

Again a rectangle with area 2; the sides differ only by $\frac{1}{204}$.
   Once more:

$$a_4 = \frac{1}{2}(a_3 + b_3) = \frac{577}{408},$$

$$b_4 = \frac{2}{a_4} = \frac{816}{577}.$$

The difference between the sides is now $\frac{1}{235416}$.

   We can continue in this way as far as we please:

$$a_{n+1} = \frac{1}{2}(a_n + b_n),$$

$$b_{n+1} = \frac{2}{a_{n+1}}.$$

Such a definition of a sequence of numbers is called *recursive*. Now $a_n$ is a fraction,

$$a_n = \frac{p_n}{q_n}.$$

$$b_n = \frac{2q_n}{p_n}.$$

$$a_{n+1} = \frac{p_n^2 + 2q_n^2}{2p_nq_n},$$

i.e.

$$p_{n+1} = p_n^2 + 2q_n^2,$$

$$q_{n+1} = 2p_nq_n.$$

We consider

$$a_n - b_n = \frac{p_n^2 - 2q_n^2}{p_nq_n}$$

more closely, and in particular the numerator

$$z_n = p_n^2 - 2q_n^2.$$

One gets

$$z_{n+1} = p_{n+1}^2 - 2q_{n+1}^2 = (p_n^2 + 2q_n^2)^2 - 8p_n^2q_n^2$$
$$= (p_n^2 - 2q_n^2)^2.$$

Thus

$$z_{n+1} = z_n^2.$$

Now we had $a_1 = 1$, thus $p_1 = q_1 = 1$, i.e. $z_1 = -1$.
   Continued squaring gives

$$z_n = 1$$

for all $n > 1$, i.e.

$$a_n - b_n = \frac{1}{p_n q_n}.$$

The difference between the sides gets small quickly. In order to see this, we also estimate the denominator. We have

$$q_n \geqslant 2^{2^{n-1}-1},$$

since this is true for $n = 1$, and if it is taken as true for $q_n$, we get

$$q_{n+1} = 2p_n q_n > 2q_n^2 \geqslant 2 \cdot \left(2^{2^{n-1}-1}\right)^2 = 2^{2^n-1}.$$

It thus follows that for the denominator

$$p_n q_n \geqslant q_n^2 \geqslant 2^{2^n-2}.$$

$$a_n - b_n = \frac{1}{p_n q_n} \leqslant 2^{-2^n+4}$$

does indeed become very small very quickly.

We have so arranged it that

$$a_n b_n = 2.$$

$a_n$ $(n \geqslant 1)$ is somewhat larger than $\sqrt{2}$ and $b_n$ somewhat smaller. $\sqrt{2}$ lies between $a_n$ and $b_n$, which differ slightly. We can enclose $\sqrt{2}$ between rational numbers as accurately as we please, but $\sqrt{2}$ is itself not rational. Still the approximation can be continued indefinitely – ad infinitum.

# 3 What computers can do

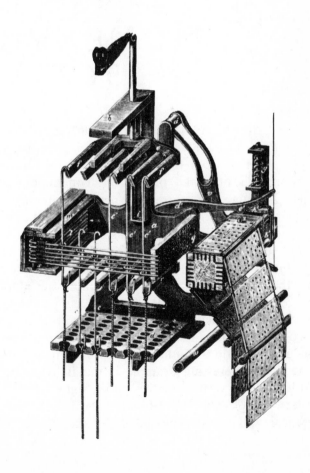

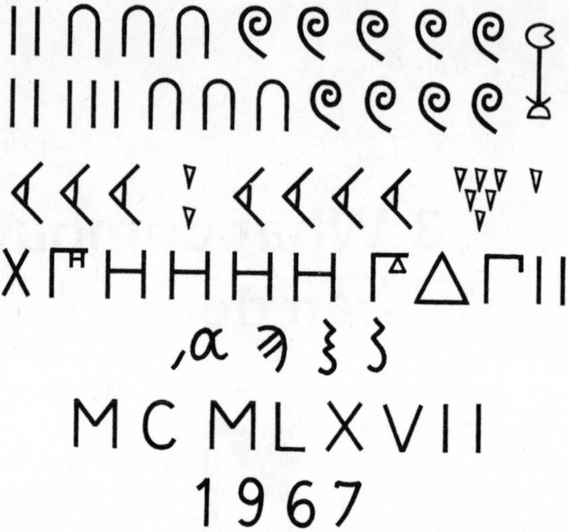

**Figure 3·1**

Figure 3·1 above shows the number 1967 as written by an ancient Egyptian, a Babylonian, a Greek from the time of Homer and one from the age of Pericles, a European of Charlemagne's time and one of our contemporaries. The ancient Egyptian has written the necessary numbers of the signs for 1000, 100, 10 and 1, ordered from right to left. The Homeric Greek in the fourth line uses symbols for 1000, 500, 100, 50, 10, 5, 1 and orders them from left to right, while the other Greek in the fifth line is more concise at the cost of using the entire Greek alphabet to denote the numbers 1, 2, . . ., 9, 10, 20, . . ., 90, 100, 200, . . ., 900, beginning again at 1000, which is denoted by an $a$ ($=1$) with a dash added. The so-called Roman numerals in the fifth line scarcely need explaining. Nor do the indo-arabic ones in line seven.

The most interesting example is the Babylonian in the third line. The 7 vertical wedges on the right denote 7 units, the next 4 hooks on their left stand for 4 tens. Then come 2 vertical wedges counting 60 each, and finally 3 hooks counting 600 each; thus altogether $3 \times 600 + 2 \times 60 + 4 \times 10 + 7 \times 1 = 1967$.

The Babylonians had a system based on 60, not only for their numerals but also for their money, weights and measures. There are still traces of it. Our division of hours and degrees into 60 minutes and of minutes into 60 seconds derives from the Babylonians.

It is remarkable that 60 played so important a role for the Babylonians. It is even more remarkable that they used the same signs for 1, 60, $60^2$, ... and indeed for $60^{-1}$, $60^{-2}$, ..., and again the same signs for 10, $10 \times 60$, etc. But we should have some feeling for this ourselves. Of the two symbols 6 in 66 one stands for a real 6 and the other for 60.

Our number system is called positional. Moving a given digit one place to the left multiplies its value by a factor of ten; while moving it to the right, possibly beyond the decimal point, divides its value by ten. The Babylonian system, too, was positional, but with base 60 instead of 10; unfortunately the lack of a zero made it somewhat inconvenient in practice.

Why do we use 10? Well, of course, because names for numbers are based on the decimal system, even if this nomenclature is not positional, but uses new names each time for 10, 100, 1000, 1000000. And of course the decimal system of our language derives from our fingers and toes, on which men learnt to count and reckon. From a mathematical point of view it is just as arbitrary and conventional as the system based on 60.

The most natural system mathematically would be a

dyadic system with only two digits, 0 and 1.

## Dyadic system

How would 1967 be expressed in such a system?

$$11110101111$$

The reader can check it. Working from the right we have 1 units, 1 two, 1 four, 1 eight, etc., while the 1 on the extreme left stands for $2^{10} = 1024$. It is easy to obtain the expression of 1967 in the dyadic system:

| | |
|---:|:---|
| 1967 | |
| 983 | 1 |
| 491 | 1 |
| 245 | 1 |
| 122 | 1 |
| 61 | 0 |
| 30 | 1 |
| 15 | 0 |
| 7 | 1 |
| 3 | 1 |
| 1 | 1 |
| 0 | 1 |

We divide successively by 2, and write the remainder (0 or 1) on the right. The remainders, written from right to left instead of from top to bottom give the dyadic representation.

This is a very practical system. The addition and multiplication tables are as follows:

$$0 + 0 = 0, \qquad 0 + 1 = 1, \qquad 1 + 0 = 1, \qquad 1 + 1 = 10,$$
$$0 \times 0 = 0, \qquad 0 \times 1 = 0, \qquad 1 \times 0 = 0, \qquad 1 \times 1 = 1;$$

There are only eight formulae, instead of the two hundred which have to be memorised for the decimal system.

Knowing these rules, one can calculate, just as in the decimal system:

```
    100101              1000011             1101
  +  11110            −   11110           × 101
  ─────────           ─────────           ──────
   1000011              100101             1101
                                           1101
                                          ───────
                                          1000001
```

This represents $37 + 30 = 67$, $67 - 30 = 37$ and $13 \times 5 = 65$.

Long division, that stumbling-block for beginners, presents no difficulty at all. One has only to check whether the divisor can be subtracted or not, and write a 1 or an 0 accordingly:

```
              1101
           ─────────
    101  │ 1000001
           101
           ───
           110
           101
           ───
            101
            101
            ───
```

## Nim

A small digression, to show what can be done with the dyadic system.

The game of Nim is said to come from China. Several heaps of matches are laid on the table. Two players take turns to take away matches. A player can take matches from one heap only, and is allowed to take a whole heap if he wishes. The winner is the one who takes the last match.

Suppose the heaps contain

$$10, 4, 7, 3$$

matches. I go first and take the whole heap of 10 away. Suppose you then take 2 from the 7, leaving

$$4, 5, 3.$$

Next I take 2 from the 3, and you take 2 from the 5, leaving

$$4, 3, 1.$$

Now I take 2 from the heap of 4. You give up, don't you?

What is the clue to such a game? Let us write the given numbers 10, 4, 7, 3 in the dyadic system:

$$1010$$
$$100$$
$$111$$
$$11$$

In the first column there is one 1, in the second there are two, in the third three and in the fourth two. Thus there is at least one column having an odd number of 1's. Whenever this is the case, the player who begins can make sure of winning. Each time he plays, he has only to make the number of 1's in each column even. I did this when I took away the whole of the first heap. After this, whatever you do, you will make new columns in which the number of 1's is odd. After your first turn it was

$$100$$
$$101$$
$$11$$

The second column contains an odd number of 1's. I took two from the last heap, thus making each column even. After your next turn you left

$$100$$
$$11$$
$$1$$

and so it goes on. The winning move produces the smallest possible even number of 1's, namely 0, while any of your moves leaves at least one column containing an odd number of 1's. Thus I must be the winner.

Suppose we begin with

$$27 = 11011$$
$$5 = \phantom{00}101$$
$$17 = 10001,$$

and I make the 27 into 20 = 10100, then however you play, I win, provided I make no mistakes. On the other hand, starting with

$$31 = 11111$$
$$7 = \phantom{00}111$$
$$24 = 11000$$

and if I play first, I cannot win unless you make a mistake.

## As quickly as you can

What is

$$7489 \times 9126?$$

Be as quick as you can! Time yourself with a stopwatch! You can congratulate yourself if you work it out in half a minute. You have to write down 27 figures to do it.

How long would it take to do a million such sums? There are half a million minutes in a year, and so it would take you a whole year, without allowing any time for food, sleep or relaxation. And how many of the answers would be correct?

A modern computer does 10,000 of these calculations in half a minute and more than a million per hour. Machines are getting faster – soon they will be able to cope with a million such calculations in half a minute.

Are we in such a hurry?

## Wait a moment

Computing can be an absorbing occupation, but it can also be tedious. To err is human, and as long as men make computations they will make mistakes. An incorrect answer is usually worse than none at all.

From ancient times instruments have been used in calculation. Working on paper is actually a rather recent invention. In antiquity and in the middle ages people worked with counters on a board, or with beads on an abacus. This is said to be usual among the Chinese even now. Since the 17th-century inventors have attempted to construct computing machines and mass-production began in the 19th century. In the 20th century hand-operated machines have had to give way to electrical ones.

However, mathematics and the possibilities of applying it have developed much faster than have computing machines. Computation is not the same thing as mathematics. In this book, for instance, there is a lot about mathematics but hardly any computation.

Let us take some examples.

In his great work of 1687 Newton set up the laws which are still the basis of celestial mechanics. These laws can be expressed in formulae, called differential equations, which have to be solved if we want to calculate the motions of the heavenly bodies. The positions and velocities of the members of our solar system at a certain time are determined by observation, and once these are known, the positions of the planets, moons and comets can then be calculated for all future (and past) times. Newton himself could decide only in very broad outline whether his theory agreed with observation. Even the moon's orbit was too difficult for Newton and his successors because it required too much computation.

This was unfortunate, because the knowledge of the moon's orbit was at that time an important practical question. The problem of fixing the position of a ship at sea would have been solved immediately, had one been able to provide the captains with exact lunar tables. Really satisfactory tables for the motions of the heavenly bodies have been produced only recently, and in fact with the aid of the new computers. The theory of their motions is quite simple, the equations can easily be written down, but the numerical solution of the equations requires millions of calculations. In the last century hundreds of people were employed for years on these calculations. Today a computer does the same work in a few days or weeks.

In this respect celestial mechanics is still quite simple. Atmospheric motions, the tides, the circulation of water or air around a ship's hull or an aeroplane's wing, the waves emitted by an atom or a radio antenna or the movements of prices or capital in a nation's economy are mathematically much more complicated problems. Considerable simplifications are introduced in these problems in order to attack them at all, and even then they demand so much computation that ever larger and faster computers have to be built to deal with them.

Do you want to know tomorrow's weather exactly? In theory this can be worked out, and with the aid of a large computer this can actually be done numerically. However, you must be rather patient – it takes about a year. Can you wait as long as that?

When, half a century ago, the Dutch wanted to enclose the

Zuyder Zee, they naturally wanted to know the necessary height and form of the dam. Experiments were made with models, in which the motions of wind and water were reproduced on a small scale so as to find out how the tides would change under the influence of a dam. At that time computers were not far enough advanced to be of much assistance. Today, in the much more ambitious delta-plan for closing all but one of the mouths of the Rhine, Meuse and Scheldt, computers are indispensable. There are many questions which have to be answered by computation, from the movement of water in the great basin of the North Sea to the increase in strength of the currents as the mouths are narrowed and closed.

In many countries there are now agencies, which forecast the development of the economy, production, the state of employment, prices, wages, consumption and capital investment for the coming year, and the influences which the Government's financial measures can have on this development. It might have been possible to do this kind of thing in the past, but how long would the calculations have taken? The measures necessary in 1965 would not have been worked out until 1980. It has only become a practical possibility with the faster computers.

Using a radar echo one can determine the distance but not the direction of a space ship. However, the ship's path can be worked out if one knows the manner in which its distance changes with time. It is necessary to know the precise position and velocity of the space ship at the instant when the astronaut is given the signal to land, that is to fire the retro-rockets. The essential calculations must be carried out by the base station in a fraction of a second. A similar lightning rapidity is needed in calculating the moment for opening the camera shutter in a space probe to photograph the moon or Mars. We raised the question: 'Are we in such a hurry?' Urgency is a relative matter. If the calculations for the delta plan took a century, the project might as well be abandoned. If the budget for 1966 is in preparation, one cannot tell the Chancellor of the Exchequer: 'Wait until 1980 and I'll be able to tell you whether purchase tax should be reduced in 1966'. It is no use radioing the astronaut, who is concerned with thousandth parts of seconds: 'Wait a moment'.

## Automation

Chapter 2 of this book contains an elegant method of calculating $\sqrt{2}$ to higher and higher accuracy. The method is to start with a rough approximation $a_1(=1)$ and to calculate successively

$$b_1 = \frac{2}{a_1}$$

$$a_2 = \frac{1}{2}(a_1 + b_1)$$

$$b_2 = \frac{2}{a_2}$$

$$a_3 = \frac{1}{2}(a_2 + b_2) \text{ etc.,}$$

so obtaining closer and closer limits between which $\sqrt{2}$ lies.

Such methods of solving equations are very common. The equation is written in a form

$$f(x) = x,$$

where $x$ is the unknown, and an initial rough approximation $x_1$ is substituted in the left hand side to calculate

$$f(x_1) = x_2.$$

From $x_2$ one calculates the value $x_3$ by

$$f(x_2) = x_3,$$

and in general

$$f(x_n) = x_{n+1};$$

if the form chosen for the equation is suitable, the difference between successive values $x_n$ becomes smaller and smaller, and the values approximate to the solution of the equation

$$f(x) = x.$$

The invention of a process for calculating $\sqrt{2}$ or the solution of much more complicated equations more and more exactly is a problem for a mathematician. The actual calculation can then be left to a computer. The latter needs only to be able to do arithmetic, or, if he has a calculating machine, not even this. In that case he need know only how to feed the numbers in, which knob to press and how to read off the result. In the case of $\sqrt{2}$ the mathematician gives him the following orders:

Set the number $a$ in register II (divisor), the number 2 in register I (dividend) and press Key D (division). Clear register I, transfer the contents of register III $(\frac{2}{a})$ to register I and press Key A (addition). Clear registers I and II, transfer the result of register III $(a + \frac{2}{a})$ to register I, set a 2 in register II and press Key D. Register III will now show $\frac{1}{2}(a + \frac{2}{a})$. Record the number in register III and, calling this new number $a$, repeat the process from the beginning. Continue until the last new $a$ differs from its predecessor at most in the last decimal place.

The calculator can execute this order, because he is actually capable of more than turning handles and pressing keys. He understands the order, and knows what he has to do at each stage to carry it out. If we want to entrust the order to a machine the machine must be able to do more than calculate. It must be able to understand orders and carry them out in succession, and must be able to turn itself off when a certain result has been attained. There are many such machines: the machine which ejects a postage stamp when a coin is inserted, the iron which turns itself off by thermostatic control, the record player which turns itself off when the record is finished, and perhaps even puts on a new record and turns itself on again. One of the first examples of this type of machine was the loom invented by the Frenchman J. M. Jacquard (1752–1834) to weave complicated patterns automatically. Instead of a weaver who raises certain threads of the warp according to given instructions and passes through a shuttle with a thread of a certain colour, the loom is controlled by punched cards on a long ribbon. When a hole appears at a certain place corresponding levers are engaged, and their motion ensures that warp and woof combine in the desired manner.

## Controls and memory

To work automatically, a computing machine must have not only an *apparatus for calculating*, but also *controls*, which govern the machine's operation, and a *memory*, in which the given data and requirements and the results of intermediate stages in the calculations can be stored until they are needed. The idea of such a machine is due to the Englishman Charles Babbage (1792–1871). The fruits of his strenuous labours got no further than the Science Museum in Kensington. It was still a century too early for these plans: technology, especially electrical technology, was not sufficiently developed. More successful were the much more modest but realistic plans of the American H. Hollerith (1860–1929), the father of punched-card machines, such as every comparatively large firm uses today. Not until the rise of the electronics industry did the great enterprise of building really large automatic computers succeed. 'Really large' refers not to the size of the machines, but to their performance, speed and the capacity of their memories. With transistors and printed circuits the 'giant computers' of today are physically smaller than their 'dwarf' predecessors of twenty years ago.

For a computer to work it must be given instructions.

Suppose

$$24789 \times 345$$

is to be worked out. With a hand-operated machine the 24789 is set in the register, is added five times into the product register; this is then moved one place to the right and the 24789 added four times into the product register, which now shows $45 \times 24789$; finally the product register is moved another place to the right and the 24789 is added three times, to produce the desired product.

Electric calculating machines are more automatic. The two numbers 24789 and 345 are set in two registers, and the multiplication key is pressed. The machine then carries out automatically the steps described above.

Electronic computers work quite differently. There are no registers, cogs, cranks or digits to set and read off. The machine's input is a punched tape, while an electric typewriter finally types the results on long sheets of paper.

The tape contains data and instructions: numbers to be processed, and individual instructions for dealing with them. The input may indeed include a whole table of logarithms, which the machine is to consult when required. It might also include a general method, say, of extracting square roots, or of solving systems of $n$ simultaneous first degree equations in $n$ unknowns, or even two such methods, of which the machine must choose the more suitable in each case.

What the machine reads on the punched tape it stores in its memory. Tape recorders are familiar machines, in which speech is recorded on magnetic tape, which retains and can reproduce the speech until it has been erased. The computer contains a similar device: a rapidly rotating magnetic drum, whose contents can be read off in a fraction of a second. On this the instructions are stored, and to it the machine brings intermediate results which will be used again later. However, the machine has further storage, 'high-speed storage', resembling a television screen, on which cathode rays write and read off digits. These are used for results which will be needed quickly, within a hundred thousandth part of a second rather than a hundredth of a second.

Of course the places where something is stored in the memory must be numbered. The instructions might read: take the contents of address 3456, multiply them by 2, and transfer the result to address 218, or perhaps to an unoccupied address, which the machine selects and whose number it then notes in some prescribed place.

The final results of the calculations go into the memory, the magnetic drum, whence they are dictated to the electric typewriter or made up into a graph. This process is much slower than the computation. When the process of calculation is over and the computer is already working on new problems, the typewriter can still spend hours copying the results from the magnetic drum. The scientist, whether physicist, astronomer, biologist or economist, pores over the long streamers of figures, anxious whether the results agree with his observations and whether his mathematical theories give a satisfactory explanation of the behaviour of nature or society.

## The language of holes

What can one tell a machine by using a punched tape? The punched cards of Jacquard's loom told the levers which of them were to engage, and the rolls of a pianola work in the same way.

A punched tape is a narrow strip of paper; each line of the strip has room for 5 holes. Sometimes 5 are punched, sometimes none, and sometimes 1, 2, 3 or 4 at the appropriate places on a given line. How many different possible pieces of information (different ways of punching) correspond to one line of the strip? Write instead of 'no hole' a '0' and instead of 'a hole' a '1', and put the 0's and 1's in the appropriate places. Then the possible arrangements for the line are

$$
\begin{array}{ccccc}
0 & 0 & 0 & 0 & 0 \\
0 & 0 & 0 & 0 & 1 \\
0 & 0 & 0 & 1 & 0 \\
0 & 0 & 0 & 1 & 1 \\
0 & 0 & 1 & 0 & 0 \\
0 & 0 & 1 & 0 & 1 \\
\end{array}
$$

and so on, ending with

$$
\begin{array}{ccccc}
1 & 1 & 1 & 0 & 0 \\
1 & 1 & 1 & 0 & 1 \\
1 & 1 & 1 & 1 & 0 \\
1 & 1 & 1 & 1 & 1.
\end{array}
$$

What does this remind us of? These are the numbers from

0 to 31 written in the dyadic system. Thus there are $32 = 2^5$ possibilities for each line.

The number

$$99999999$$

is represented in the dyadic system by

$$00010 . 11111 . 01011 . 11000 . 00111 . 11111 .$$

Thus decimal numbers of up to 8 figures require at most 27 figures in the diadic system and can be written in punched code on 6 lines of the tape.

Not only numbers can be coded in this way. If the letters of the alphabet are numbered and represented by the corresponding number, every letter can be written as a combination of punched holes in one line of the strip. After representing the 26 letters there are still 6 combinations left over, which can be used to indicate spaces between words and the comma, semicolon, full stop, etc.

The alternatives of punching a hole or not form one of the many ways of making concrete the abstract notions of 0 and 1. The punched tape passes between five electrical contacts, which it insulates, but where a hole appears contact is made, and an electric current flows through a conductor. Thus at the contact the alternatives 'no hole – hole' are translated into 'no current – current'. The current flows to the magnetic drum, which is covered with ferrite crystals. The current activates an electromagnet placed opposite the rotating magnetic drum and those of the drum's crystals which are immediately opposite the magnet become magnetised and remain tiny magnets until their magnetism is erased. Thus 'no hole – hole' (and ultimately 0, 1) is translated into 'unmagnetised – magnetised'. When the drum is read, a magnetic spot on the drum induces an electric current which flows away somewhere else. This current might flow to a switch, where 'unmagnetised – magnetised' is turned into 'off – on'; or to a vacuum tube where it becomes 'charged – uncharged'; or to a relay which may operate or not; or to a transistor, which may pass a current through or not. Everywhere the machine speaks and understands the language of 0 and 1, except at the final stage, where the numerical results are translated from the dyadic to the decimal system before they are dictated to the typewriter.

These punched tapes were not originally invented for computers, but for long distance communications. The text, which appears on the tape in the language of punched holes, is sent via a cable or through the ether; the presence or absence of a hole corresponds to the sending, or not, of an electric signal. Not only texts, but even pictures can be sent in this way, provided they are first translated into the dyadic language. How can this be done? Take a photograph, say $8 \times 16$ cm. Cover it with a grid by dividing the width into 64 equal parts, the length into 128. This gives $64 \times 128 = 2^{13}$ squares in the grid. These are numbered by two numbers, one giving the division of breadth, the other of length corresponding to a given square; the first number ranges from 0 to 63, the second from 0 to 127. Of course the numbers are written dyadically from 000000 to 111111 and from 0000000 to 1111111, so that each square is numbered by giving a sequence of 13 0's and 1's. Each cell is then scanned in order by a photoelectric cell to see if it is light or dark. This information is then put on a punched tape, where 'hole' stands for 'light' and 'no hole' for 'dark'. Alternatively the 32 various combinations of holes in a line of the tape can be used to indicate graduations of light and dark in each square. The receiver of this information can use it to piece together a copy of the original photograph.

This system is familiar from television. The scanned picture is transmitted through the ether in dyadic language and appears reconstituted on the screen of the receiver.

With television and telex it is important that what is put in at one end emerges unchanged at the other. In computers on the other hand the output appears quite different from the input, because the data have been processed in the machine.

## Processing

Processing occurs in small stages – stages so small, that each lasts only a hundred thousandth or even a millionth part of a second. The addition or multiplication of two 30-place dyadic numbers is an involved process. Its simplest components are

$$0 + 0 = 00, \qquad 0 + 1 = 01, \qquad 1 + 0 = 01, \qquad 1 + 1 = 10,$$
$$0 \times 0 = 0, \qquad 0 \times 1 = 0, \qquad 1 \times 0 = 0, \qquad 1 \times 1 = 1.$$

To given numbers $a$ and $b$, which must be 0 or 1, is assigned a product $c$ which is again either 0 or 1. In the case of

Figure 3·2

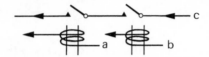

addition the sum $a + b$ may be written as a two-digit number $cd$ and there are assigned to $a$ and $b$ the number $c$ which gives the left hand digit of the sum and the number $d$ for the right hand digit. This assignment may be expressed by the table

| $a$ | $b$ | $c$ | $d$ |
|-----|-----|-----|-----|
| 0 | 0 | 0 | 0 |
| 0 | 1 | 0 | 1 |
| 1 | 0 | 0 | 1 |
| 1 | 1 | 1 | 0 |

Let us translate 0 and 1 into the language of electric currents. To $a$, $b$, $c$, $d$ correspond electric conductors. If both $a$ and $b$ carry current, so does $c$, but if at least one of $a$, $b$ carries no current, then neither does $c$. This is reminiscent of switches in series. In the circuit $c$ are two switches, one operated by $a$ and the other by $b$, say by means of relays (see figure 3·2). When current flows through $a$ and $b$, both electromagnets are activated, both contacts close and current flows in $c$; but if there is no current in even one of $a$ or $b$, the corresponding electromagnet fails to close one of the contacts and current cannot flow in $c$.

The situation in $d$ is more involved. If $a$ and $b$ agree, $d$ carries no current, while if $a$ and $b$ are different, current flows in $d$. Does this not suggest a lamp which can be turned

**Figure 3·3**                                                                          83

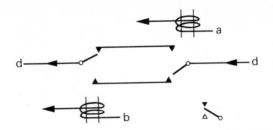

on at two switches? If both switches are in the same position the light is off, if they are in opposite positions the lamp glows.

This is depicted, using relays, in figure 3·3, where the switches are to be regarded as in the same position and there is no current in $a$ or $b$; $d$ is disconnected and no current flows in it. If a current flows in *one* of the circuits $a$ or $b$, then one electromagnet operates and one switch changes over, so that $d$ is closed and current flows; if current flows in *both* $a$ and $b$, then both electromagnets operate and $d$ is disconnected.

Two quantities $a$ and $b$, which may take the values 0 or 1, can be combined in many ways to give a new quantity $x$, which again takes either 0 or 1 as values. The table

| $a$ | $b$ | $x$ |
|-----|-----|-----|
| 0 | 0 | $x_1$ |
| 0 | 1 | $x_2$ |
| 1 | 0 | $x_3$ |
| 1 | 1 | $x_4$ |

indicates that $x$ takes the values $x_1$, $x_2$, $x_3$ and $x_4$ respectively, corresponding to the four possible combinations 00, 01, 10, 11 of $a$ and $b$. There are 16 such processes for combining $a$ and $b$ into a new quantity $x$ and each of these 16 can be represented by a switching circuit like those for $c$ and $d$. It is also possible to start with a single quantity $a$ instead of a pair and to construct a new $x$ from it

| $a$ | $x$ |
|---|---|
| 0 | $x_1$ |
| 1 | $x_2$; |

this can be done in four ways: $x_1$ and $x_2$ can be both 0 or both 1, or $x$ can agree with $a$ or be opposite to $a$.

## Truth tables

The use of tables, such as those above, becomes clear if 1 and 0 are interpreted as 'true' and 'false', respectively, and the $a, b, \ldots, x$ as statements which may be true or false. Operation on two such statements may produce a new compound statement. For example:

$a$ 1 December is not a Sunday.
$b$ 2 December is not a Sunday.
$x$ 1 December is not a Sunday, *or* 2 December is not a Sunday.
$y$ 1 December is not a Sunday, *and* 2 December is not a Sunday.
$z$ *If* 1 December is not a Sunday, *then* 2 December is not a Sunday.

The statement $x$ is always true, regardless of whether $a$ and $b$ are true or false, because of two successive days at least one is not a Sunday. (We always understand 'or' in the sense that '$a$ or $b$' remains true in the case when both $a$ and $b$ are true.) On the other hand $y$ is true in some years and not in others. Similarly with $z$, which is false when 1 December is not a Sunday, but 2 December is, i.e. whenever 1 December falls on a Saturday.

Further examples:

$a$  1 December is a Sunday.
$b$  Christmas Day falls on 1 December.
$c$  Christmas Day falls on 25 December.
$d$  New Year's Day falls on 1 January.
$e$  Easter falls on 2 January.

In this case the statements

> $c$ and $d$,
> $a$ or $c$,
> $d$ or $e$,
> if $b$, then $c$,
> if $b$, then $e$,

are always true, while

> $b$ and $c$,
> $b$ and $e$,
> $b$ or $e$,
> if $c$, then $e$,

are always false; the statements

> $a$ or $b$,
> $a$ and $c$,
> if $a$, then $b$,

are sometimes true and sometimes false. For example, the last is false in years when 1 December is a Sunday, for if the statement were true in this case, Christmas Day would have to fall on 1 December.

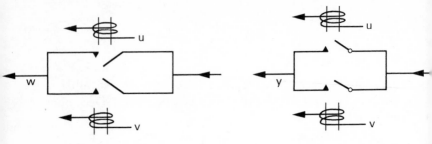

**Figure 3·4**          **Figure 3·5**

Let $u$ and $v$ be two statements, of which I know only whether they are true or false. I can then say whether the compound statements, '$u$ and $v$', '$u$ or $v$', 'if $u$, then $v$' are true or false. '$u$ and $v$' is true only when both $u$ and $v$ are true, '$u$ or $v$' is false only when both $u$ and $v$ are false, and 'if $u$, then $v$' is false only when $u$ is true, but $v$ false.

Let us replace true and false by 1 and 0. Then we have found that the conjunctions 'and', 'or' and 'if, then' operate on $u$ and $v$ according to the following table:

| $u$ | $v$ | $u$ and $v$ | $u$ or $v$ | if $u$, then $v$ |
|---|---|---|---|---|
| 0 | 0 | 0 | 0 | 1 |
| 0 | 1 | 0 | 1 | 1 |
| 1 | 0 | 0 | 1 | 0 |
| 1 | 1 | 1 | 1 | 1 |

'And' operates like multiplication and can be represented by the same switching circuit, i.e. the circuit for $c$ in the last paragraph. 'Or' can be represented by switches in parallel ($w$ in figure 3·4).

'$u$ or $v$' is without current only when both $u$ and $v$ are without current.

'If $u$, then $v$' is represented by $y$ in figure 3·5.

'If $u$, then $v$' is without current only when $u$ flows and $v$ does not.

The switching circuit of figure 3·3 can also be interpreted in

**Figure 3·6**                                                                87

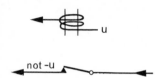

the language of 'true' and 'false'. Then $d$ is the statement '$a$ and $b$ contradict one another'.

Instead of operation on two statements to produce a new one we may start from a single one and obtain a new statement, for example by negating it. From $u$ is obtained 'not $u$' as illustrated by the table

| $u$ | not $u$ |
|-----|---------|
| 0   | 1       |
| 1   | 0       |

and figure 3·6.

When no current flows in $u$, a current flows in not-$u$, and conversely. 'And', 'or', 'if, then', '. . . contradict each other', 'not . . .', etc. are called *logical operations*, because they operate not so much on individual statements as on truth and falsehood. Logic has a great deal to do with thought and we shall have to deal later with thought in machines.

## Machines which play games

By now our reasons for explaining Nim have become clear. The rules of play and the secret of winning are so simple that they can be explained to a quite primitive machine. What are the requirements for such a machine? It must be able to translate numbers from the decimal to the dyadic system, it must be able to count the number of 1's in a column and recognize whether this number is odd or even and it must be able, whenever this is possible, to reduce one of the given numbers in such a way that the number of 1's in each column becomes even. Every engineer familiar with switching circuits can design such a machine quickly and cheaply.

In the Chicago world fair after the war a machine which played Nim was exhibited and this was later brought to Europe. It weighed several tons, but this was bluff: it could have been installed in an ordinary radio cabinet. The machine behaved like a gentleman and always offered its opponent a configuration in which the opponent could make sure of winning, but even so it usually won. The opponents did not know the secret of winning or, if they did, they were unable to reckon as quickly and accurately as the machine. The impresario of this marvel noticed in time that its superhuman speed depressed the public. To avoid a fiasco, the machine was artificially slowed down. It was made not to answer immediately, but to pretend to be considering its move.

When one thinks of automata playing games one usually thinks not so much of machines which play Nim well, but of games of chance such as coin tossing, dice or roulette in an automated form. In the long run a true coin comes down as often heads as it does tails. In this respect it is reliable. In other respects it is quite unreliable and this is the essence of games of chance. Whether the coin will fall heads or tails at the next throw is quite unpredictable, even after long observation of the coin. The same applies to dice or roulette. If one of the roulette wheels in the casino at Monte Carlo exhibited regularities the wheel would be repaired at once.

In many countries games of chance for money are forbidden. The owners of the well-known 'fruit machines' assert with some justice that these are games of skill: the machines are usually so cheaply made and so decrepit that experiments show up regularities in their behaviour and even possibilities of influencing them. In the case of one machine investigated the player had a chance of 60% of winning his money back and with skill he could raise this to 70%. That is to say, of every pound he puts in, he loses 8/– on the average if he plays at random, while if he plays cleverly he can reduce the average loss to 6/– in the pound. Of course the really clever player is the one who does not play at all, for his average loss is zero. It has been suggested that instead of trying hopelessly to combat these machines, one should have a law obliging the operators to state clearly on each machine the average respective losses of players playing blindly or skilfully. This should certainly be the most effective measure against the gambling-machine craze.

## Matching pennies

We shall presently discuss a quite different kind of game-playing machine.

In the game of matching pennies two players A and B produce one coin each, simultaneously. If the coins match (two heads or two tails) A wins and if not B wins. A and B have essentially equal chances. However, skill does play a role in this game. If B, say, is so foolish as to play alternately heads and tails, A has only to imitate him in order to win.

If A adopts this foolish strategy, B can simply play the opposite one and he will win. Of course no one will be as silly as this, but a little foolishness will be enough to cause losses, if the opponent is cleverer. The player who can see through the strategy of his opponent has an advantage. For this reason it is the best policy to play without any plan, showing heads or tails at random. If one has no strategy, it cannot be discovered; if one plays according to no fixed rule, the opponent can get no profit from any strategy. Now it is not so easy to produce randomness; imperceptibly one falls into patterns in the long run. We once had people write down sequences of numbers and found a repetition of patterns of numbers, somehow connected with birthdays, house and telephone numbers.

C.E.Shannon once made use of this human tendency to regularity to build a machine, which plays matching pennies with a human opponent and wins 60% of the games on the average, although both the machine and the player should have equal chances of winning. Instead of heads and tails the symbols 0 and 1 are used. The human player chooses one of two keys, 0 and 1, and presses it, and the machine produces a 0 or 1 simultaneously. If both choices are the same the machine wins; otherwise the man wins. The game is played for some time and meanwhile the machine notes in its memory what has gone before. When the game has lasted some time, the machine analyses the results and the behaviour of its opponents, and makes use of the patterns it discovers there. With its long memory and lightning speed of calculation the machine discovers its opponent's plans, even unconscious ones. One can only protect oneself against this and get rid of even unconscious plans by tossing a coin and pressing key 0 or 1 according to whether the coin falls heads or tails. This is surely also the machine's strategy at the beginning of the game, when it does not yet know enough about its opponent and must at all events itself avoid being seen through.

Thus Shannon's machine must not only calculate but also play at tossing coins. It must be able to work not only in an orderly but also a random manner. It must be capable of generating random sequences of zeros and ones. This applies not only to game-playing machines. There are all kinds of practical problems for whose solution it is appropriate to make the computer play a game of chance. One then speaks of 'Monte-Carlo methods'.

## Monte Carlo methods

We begin with an example. Electric power stations can reckon with a certain average current load, but their capacity must be considerably higher than this average if the stations are also to cope with the peak loads. Such peaks are in general well-known, e.g. dark winter evenings when domestic and street lighting and electric signs are switched on while the factories are still drawing their power. There are also unexpected peaks, accumulations of random events, e.g. a cold snap in which many electric fires are turned on, coinciding with a sensational television programme to which a vast public tunes in. All at once the generators become overloaded and cut out. It is perhaps impossible to avoid this sort of thing completely, but it should not happen too often. To calculate the frequency of such undesirable overloading is a mathematical problem. The method of attack is indicated in a somewhat simpler case. Consider the power station supplying a large electric railway system. If, owing to an oversight in the timetables or to chance delays very many trains depart at the same time, an undesirable overloading may occur. This is to be avoided. The method is to set an electric computer to, so to speak, play over the complete timetable, with the introduction of all manner of randomly distributed delays, and to calculate the corresponding load on the power station in each case. In this way we get information about the random distribution of peak loads and can make corresponding decisions about the necessary capacity of the power station.

Running over the behaviour of a model in this way is called *simulation*. One might take, say, a model of the economy with producers and consumers, buyers and sellers, lenders and borrowers, and run it through with all kinds of random factors. A machine which can simulate this must be able to play games of chance. This need not involve actually throwing coins: there are many ingenious ways in which computers can produce random sequences of 0's and 1's.

## Causal machines

A distinction is made between causal machines, which process the material supplied to them entirely according to definite rules, and machines where random elements play a role. The output of a causal machine is completely determined by the input. If the same material is fed to a twin machine, both machines give exactly the same results. If, on the other hand, random elements occur in the machine, then (corresponding to a fixed input) the output is sometimes one thing and sometimes another, as in a lottery where one drawing differs from the next.

It should be noted that the causal computer is an idealisation. To err is not only human: even machines can err. A machine making millions of operations per second will occasionally make mistakes: a contact or a valve can fail or a transistor become overheated. Such failures need not affect the final result decisively, but there can be slight variations even for the same input. In practice there are no causal computers in the sense we have defined although they are conceivable as an ideal case.

On the other hand it is a remarkable fact that causally generated sequences of digits can appear to be random. For example, give a machine an 8 figure number $a$, multiply by 23, divide the product by $10^8 + 1$ and write the remainder as a new number $a$. The sequence of numbers $a$ generated in this way, when written in succession to form a sequence exhibits no recognizable regularity. With a machine working like this one could run a gambling den, yet assert that chance plays no role, that the number sequence is completely regular and that anyone wishing to break the bank need only watch the game for a while, in order to guess the system. Such an assertion is humbug. Perhaps a much larger computer would be capable of guessing the system: it is beyond the powers of a man, for whom it is as random a sequence as in Monte Carlo, and the success of his guesses is a matter of luck.

## What can causal computers do?

Or rather, what can they not do? This is to be discussed with mathematical precision. But first we have to explain exactly what a causal computer is. This was formulated by A. M. Turing (1912–54), after whom such machines are named.

The action of a Turing machine is as follows. It can read and write. What it reads from and writes on is a paper strip divided into a string of squares. The strip is bounded in one direction but extends to infinity in the other. Each square may contain one 0 or one 1 and the machine can write 0's and 1's. Starting with a given square in view, the machine reads its content and performs one of the following actions: it orders the paper strip to move on one place, or back one place, so that it can see the succeeding or preceding square; or it writes a 0 or 1 in the square it is looking at, or it changes a 0 to a 1 or vice versa. The machine's action, however, depends not only on what it has just read but on its 'internal state' at this stage. It is capable of a finite number of such internal states, labelled $S_1, S_2, \ldots, S_N$.

To simplify a little: suppose that the zeros are not written at all. Then if a square contains no symbol, this is regarded as containing a 0. To write a 0 in a square means to do nothing if the square is already empty but to rub out a 1 if there is one in the square.

The working of the machine can then be expressed thus:

1 A stroke is written in the square the machine is looking at (if the square already contains one, nothing happens). This is indicated by 1.

2 A stroke is removed from the square (or if the square is already empty, it is left so). This is indicated by 0.

3 The strip moves on one place and the following square comes into view. This is indicated by $+$.

4 The strip moves back one place and the preceding square comes into view. This is indicated by $-$.

5 Before looking at a certain square the machine changes to a new internal state $S_i$. This is indicated by $S_i$.

The paper strip is unbounded in the forward, positive direction. In the backward, negative direction lies some definite starting point, and the machine cannot move back beyond this first square without stopping. When the machine begins to function there can already be strokes written in a finite number of squares of the strip. The machine looks at the first square and its internal state is $S_1$. From here on the working is automatic. If at some stage the machine stops, the result is a strip with a finite number of ones in certain squares, which is an uninteresting result because such sequences of symbols could also be produced by non-automatic means. It is more interesting if the machine works on without ever stopping. It can then gradually generate an infinite sequence of zeros and ones, like, for instance, the number $\pi$ expressed in the dyadic system. This is a possible but not a necessary result of perpetual operation. It is also conceivable that the machine might spend its time writing a 1 in one or more squares, rubbing out what it had written, writing it again, rubbing it out, and so on for ever. That an infinite sequence really results on the strip can only be asserted when, for every given square there is a fixed moment in the machine's operation, after which the content of the square is left unaltered.

*Example 1*
The machine is supposed to have only one internal state $S$. Its actions are

$$S0 \to + 1 S, \ S1 \to + 0 S,$$

i.e. if the machine sees a 0, it writes a 1 in the next square, if it sees a 1, it writes a 0 in the next square. If the strip is empty to begin with, then the result is automatically the infinite sequence

$$0 \ 1 \ 0 \ 1 \ 0 \ 1 \ \ldots,$$

while if the first square initially contains a 1, the result is

$$1 \ 0 \ 1 \ 0 \ 1 \ 0 \ \ldots.$$

*Example 2*
This is a machine for copying a given finite sequence of symbols and writing it in a given place, say immediately after the given sequence. We shall assume that the given sequence of $n$ symbols is written in the squares with the even numbers 2, 4, . . ., $2n$, and that the sequence is to be copied into the squares numbered $2n + 2$, $2n + 4$, . . ., $4n$. The odd

numbered squares will be used for 'rough working'. In the squares immediately preceding and following the sequence, i.e. in numbers 1 and $2n + 1$, there will be a 1 to mark the beginning and end.

The machine is supposed to have 7 states $S_1, \ldots, S_7$ and its actions are

$$S_1 0 \to - - S_1,$$
$$S_1 1 \to + + 1 - S_2,$$

$$S_2 0 \to + + + S_3, \qquad\qquad S_2 1 \to + + + S_4,$$
$$S_3 0 \to + + S_3, \qquad\qquad S_4 0 \to + + S_4,$$
$$S_3 1 \to + + S_5, \qquad\qquad S_4 1 \to + + S_6,$$
$$S_5 0 \to 1 - 0 - S_7, \qquad\qquad S_6 0 \to 1 - 1 - S_7,$$
$$S_5 1 \to + + S_5, \qquad\qquad S_6 1 \to + + S_6,$$
$$S_7 0 \to - - - S_1,$$
$$S_7 1 \to - - - S_7.$$

The machine begins in state $S_1$ with a stroke in the first square. To $S_1 1$ its reaction is $+ + 1 - S_2$, i.e. it writes a stroke 1 in square 3, goes back to square 2 and changes to state $S_2$. After reading square 2 it goes on to square 5, but changes to state $S_3$ or $S_4$ depending on whether square 2 contained a 0 or a 1: this is the machine's way of remembering what was written in square 2. Let us suppose that the 5th square contains a 0, which shows that the given sequence has not yet ended. To $S_3 0$ and $S_4 0$ the machine reacts by moving on to the 7th square without changing its state. This behaviour is repeated at squares 7, 9, etc., until an odd numbered square, say the $(2n + 1)$-st is reached, which contains a 1 and indicates that the given sequence has terminated in the $(2n)$-th square. To $S_3 1$ or $S_4 1$ respectively in square $(2n + 1)$ the machine reacts by moving forward two places and changing its state to $S_5$ or $S_6$ respectively. To the 0 in square $(2n + 3)$ it reacts with $1 - 0 - S_7$ or $1 - 1 - S_7$, respectively; it makes a stroke 1 in square $(2n + 3)$, goes back and copies the content of square 2 into square $(2n + 2)$ and goes back to square $(2n + 1)$ in state $S_7$. In square $(2n + 1)$ it finds a 1 and so reacts with $S_7 1$, i.e. goes back two steps to square $(2n - 1)$, remaining in state $S_7$. In the general case $(n > 2)$ it finds a 0 there and goes back a further two steps, changing into state $S_1$, and continues moving back two steps at a time in $S_1$ until a 1 is reached, which happens in square 3. At this stage the entire process starts again, in order to copy the 4th square into the $(2n + 4)$th. The machine continues until the copying is complete and all the intermediate odd squares are filled with ones. The reader should convince himself that the machine finally runs backwards until it goes back beyond the first square and stops itself.

The given sequence has now been copied. Matters could even have been so arranged that the ones in the odd squares were erased at the end of the process.

These examples may help to convince the reader that machines of this class can carry out the four arithmetic operations, extract roots and solve equations of the $n$-th degree with integral coefficients, i.e. express the solutions as infinite dyadic fractions. Of course the coefficients must be written on the initial strip and be separated by symbols; whether a coefficient is positive or negative can be indicated, for example by one or two signs in the odd squares, while only the even squares are used to write the coefficients themselves.

It is also possible to specify a machine which factorises every natural number given into prime factors; or a machine which generates the infinite dyadic fraction expansion of $\pi$ or $e$, or of the logarithm of a given integral or algebraic number. This category also includes a machine to calculate a table of logarithms, say the logarithms of the integers to 20 places of decimals.

Is there anything which a Turing machine cannot do? This question will be discussed later on. First let us consider a different question: are these Turing machines the most general imaginable causal machines? They are certainly not the most general, because one can conceive of machines which deal with symbols other than 0 and 1, machines with several strips and several 'eyes' for scanning them, etc. These latter could be faster and more practical, but they would accomplish no more than the Turing machines. An alphabet of a finite number of symbols can always be replaced by a 0–1 alphabet; what can be accomplished simultaneously with several strips and scanners can be done successively with a single one. No exact definition of a causal machine has been given, so we cannot prove that Turing machines can do everything that the most general causal machines can. On the other hand, no one has ever described a causal machine, whose capabilities are greater than those of Turing machines, and it is improbable that this could be done. It may thus be assumed that the capabilities of causal machines are exhausted by those of the Turing machines.

## A survey of the class of Turing machines

A machine is completely known, when I know all its reactions $S_1 0, S_1 1, S_2 0, S_2 1, \ldots, S_N 0, S_N 1$, i.e. what it does when it is in each state $S_i$ and reads the symbols 0 or 1. We shall denote each such *reaction* in such a way that one $S_i$ occurs in it as the last symbol. The reactions are then ordered as above; reaction to $S_1 0$, reaction to $S_1 1$, then to $S_2 0$ and so on. The sequence of reactions written out in this way is called the *characteristic* of the machine. There is no need to include any spacing, because the occurrence of the symbols $S_i$ indicates where one reaction ends and another begins.

The possible characteristics will now be numbered according to a code. To the symbols

$$0, 1, +, -, S_1, S_2, S_3, S_4, \ldots$$

shall correspond the ciphers

$$0, 00, 01, 10, 11, 000, 001, 010, \ldots$$

respectively, which will be distributed in the even places of the code, while odd places will, in general, be filled with a 0; however, to separate symbols from one another a 1 will be written in the odd place before a symbol to indicate a space. In this code we write the reactions in order. The end of a reaction is marked by the appearance of an $S_i$.

The coded description of the machine in example 1 is:

1001100011011001101101.

This can be read as an integer in the dyadic system (2504681 in decimal notation). This is the *code number* of the machine. Following this but separated by 111 (a '111' starting at an odd-numbered place never occurs in a code number) we write the sequence of digits given initially in the strip which is to be fed into the machine. Thus we obtain a *code number* for the combination of machine and initial data. For the combination which in example 1 generates the sequence

010101 . . .

the code is

1001100011011001101101111110,

while for the combination which generates the sequence

101010 . . .

the code is

1001100011011001101101111111.

In this way all combinations of machine and initial data have been given a code number. From the code number the characteristic of the machine can be read off and the machine reconstructed, and similarly the initial data. However, it is by no means true that every natural number, written dyadically, gives the code number of a combination of machine and initial data. Even if it does so, this combination need not generate an infinite sequence of numbers. If, how-ever, this is the case, we call the integer the code number of the corresponding infinite sequence generated by machine and data. Thus

*to every infinite sequence of zeros and ones which can be generated by a machine corresponds a finite code number.*

To a given sequence there may correspond more than one number, since it is conceivable that different machines and data should generate the same infinite sequence.

If the code number of a mechanically producible sequence is given, the sequence itself is found as follows: first find the point where 111 divides the code number into the code number of the machine and that of the initial data; decipher the machine's code number, translate it into the characteristic and construct the machine; then insert the data on the strip and set the machine in motion.

We can imagine a catalogue of all mechanically producible sequences of zeros and ones: the sequences are simply ordered by their code numbers. Many of the sequences will occur more than once in the catalogue, but this does not worry us. The important thing is that none of the sequences is missing.

The set of these mechanically producible sequences is, in the terminology of chapter 2, *countable*. Now every mathe-matician knows that the set of all number sequences is more than countable. Therefore there are sequences of zeros and ones which cannot be generated by any machine with any initial data. However, we do not need to use this mathematical theorem. We can show how to construct such a sequence.

## A sequence which cannot be produced by any machine

Some natural numbers $N$ are the code numbers of mechanically producible sequences; in this case the sequence with the code number $N$ is called $C_N$. If $N$ is not the code number of such a sequence, let us nonetheless give a meaning to $C_N$ by taking it to be the sequence consisting wholly of zeros (this can indeed be produced by a machine). The sequences $C_1, C_2, \ldots$, are now written one below the other:

$$C_1: \quad a_1^{(1)}, \quad a_2^{(1)}, \quad a_3^{(1)}, \quad \ldots, \quad a_p^{(1)}, \ldots$$
$$C_2: \quad a_1^{(2)}, \quad a_2^{(2)}, \quad a_3^{(2)}, \quad \ldots, \quad a_p^{(2)}, \ldots$$
$$C_3: \quad a_1^{(3)}, \quad a_2^{(3)}, \quad a_3^{(3)}, \quad \ldots, \quad a_p^{(3)}, \ldots$$

$$C_p: \quad a_1^{(p)}, \quad a_2^{(p)}, \quad a_3^{(p)}, \quad \ldots, \quad a_p^{(p)}, \ldots$$

The $a_i(j)$ in this table are 0 or 1. Every line of the table is a mechanically producible sequence and every such sequence occurs in the table.

Let us consider the diagonal of this infinite table, starting in the top left hand corner. Change every 0 in it to a 1 and every 1 to a 0, to obtain a sequence which can be written

$$D: \quad d_1, d_2, d_3, d_4, \ldots, d_p, \ldots,$$

where

$$d_i = \begin{matrix} 1 \\ 0 \end{matrix} \quad \text{if} \quad a_i^{(i)} = \begin{matrix} 0 \\ 1 \end{matrix}$$

$D$ cannot occur as a line of the table. For $D$ is certainly not identical with $C_1$, since $D$ and $C_1$ differ at least in the first place. Neither can $D$ be identical with $C_2$, since $D$ and $C_2$ differ in the second place. In general $D$ cannot be identical with $C_p$, since $D$ and $C_p$ differ at least in the $p$-th place. Thus $D$ does not occur as a line of the table, and since the table contains all mechanically producible sequences $D$ cannot be generated by a machine. Nevertheless $D$ is not a random sequence of the type produced by tossing a coin, but a completely determined sequence.

This is a remarkable result, and is even more remarkable than at first appears. For there exists a

## Universal machine

When this universal machine is fed with a tape containing suitable data, it produces every mechanically producible sequence, and it seems inexplicable that the sequence $D$ cannot be obtained from this universal machine. We do not write down the characteristic of this universal machine. No one has yet tried to do so and it would be a waste of time, but it is easy to show how it works in principle.

If the universal machine is to produce the sequence with code number $N$, the initial data on the input strip is the code number $N$ itself. The universal machine splits $N$ up at the symbol 111 into the code number of the relevant special machine and the data which must be fed to the special machine – the secondary data strip, let us call it. The machine looks at the first square of this secondary data strip, which contains either an 0 or a 1. It then deciphers the first part of the code number of the special machine and discovers how the special machine should react to $S_1 0$ or $S_1 1$. It performs this reaction and learns also which square of the secondary strip the special machine has to look at after this reaction, and in which internal state $S_i$ it should do this. It deciphers the code number of the special machine further until it finds how the latter should react to $S_i 0$ or $S_i 1$. And so it continues, producing the sequence whose code number is $N$.

Why should the universal machine not be able to write down the sequence $D$ constructed above? It needs only to work out all the sequences $C_1$, $C_2$, . . ., successively, and indeed need only calculate each one so far that the diagonal term $a_1^{(1)}$, $a_2^{(2)}$, . . . is known, in order to alter this diagonal term, changing 0 into 1 or 1 into 0. This is quite a simple task, which the universal machine ought to be able to understand, when instructed by a strip with suitable initial data.

But we proved that $D$ cannot be produced by any machine. Is this a contradiction?

No! The problem of calculating $a_1^{(1)}$, $a_2^{(2)}$, . . . is by no means so simple. Suppose the universal machine is working out $C_p$. It is interested in the $p$-th number $a_p^{(p)}$ of $C_p$. What is this? It is what *finally* remains in the $p$-th place. Now in the $p$-th place numbers are repeatedly written and erased; how does the machine know when the $p$-th number has finally become fixed? Suppose a 0 or a 1 has remained unchanged there for a long time; how does the machine know that this will remain unchanged for ever? If $p$ is the code number of a mechanically producible sequence, then $a_p^{(p)}$ must finally become fixed – but when? There would have to be some method for the machine of deciding this, to establish $a_p^{(p)}$ and hence $d_p$ and be able to proceed to the $(p + 1)$th case. If $p$ is not the code number, in the original sense, of a mechanically producible sequence, then we have put $a_p^{(p)} = 0$. So the machine should also have to be able to decide when this is the case. We should have to build into the machine a programme, which allows it to decide such questions. Then it could write down the sequence $D$. But we have proved that it is impossible to do this.

What follows? That the universal machine cannot be so constructed that it decides all these questions. However we build the universal machine, there will be some $p$ for which the question, whether $a_p^{(p)}$ is 0 or 1, becomes undecidable and the machine gets stuck. It is quite possible that a man looking at the machine from the outside could decide the question in some ingenious way. This is a question which would not be decidable by a machine – although perhaps it could be decided in other ways.

From such concrete things as computers we have come to very abstract speculations. However, we have not yet reached the climax. We shall plunge into even deeper abstraction: those readers who find it too difficult may spare themselves and skip the rest of this subsection.

There has just been a discussion of the possibility of equipping a machine to make mathematical decisions of the type: in the construction of $C_p$ does the $p$-th place contain an 0 or a 1 in the long run? Such questions must not be decided by trial and error, but by mathematical proof. A mathematical proof consists of a finite chain of assertions, each deduced from the preceding. There is a number of fixed rules available for the deduction. The rules are completely formal; the external form of two assertions shows whether a third can be deduced from them.

We now imagine we could invent a code in which every mathematical expression, every formula and every proposition can be written numerically, using zeros and ones. Every expression, formula or proposition receives a code number from which it can be reconstructed. Similarly every proof receives a code number, which is composed of the code numbers of its constituent propositions in some way which would have to be defined more exactly. From every number can be recognized whether it is the code number of a mathematical expression, a formula, a proposition or a proof. So that the machine can do mathematics, we tell it how to recognize this property of a number. The machine can formulate the assertion

'$x$ is the code number of a proposition'

and, for each $x$, test whether this is true or not. The machine can do the same with the assertion

'$x$ is the code number of a proposition in which *one* variable occurs', *or*, with the assertion

'The proposition, whose code number is $x$, is provable.'
The machine can also write down the assertion

$Q$: 'The proposition, whose code number is $x$, is not provable', but it cannot immediately test whether $Q$ holds for a fixed $x$, since it would have to run through all proofs and see whether the proposition numbered $x$ ever came out.

Consider the last proposition, $Q$, more closely. $Q$ has a code number called $q$, say. $Q$ is a proposition involving a variable. In it replace the variable $x$ by the number $q$, so as to obtain a proposition in which no variables occur. Let this proposition be called $P$. We ask whether or not $P$ is provable?

$P$ arises, as stated, by replacing the variable $x$ in $Q$ by the number $q$ of $Q$. Thus $P$ asserts (in a rather involved form) its own unprovability. Such an assertion is unprovable, since if it could be proved, then its unprovability would be provable. Thus $P$ is unprovable, and so true or at any rate impossible to disprove.

Thus a proposition has been found, which can be neither proved nor disproved by the machine, although it is indeed to be regarded as true. If the machine runs through all the proofs of propositions, one after the other, it will never produce a proof either for this proposition or for its negation.

Admittedly this can only be asserted with certain reservations. $P$ was decided to be unprovable because otherwise both a proposition *and* its negation would have been provable. The existence of a *mechanically undecidable* proposition was deduced from the assumption that the machine cannot prove contradictory propositions.

This is the famous undecidability theorem of K. Gödel (1931). We have tried to show in a very sketchy way how it is obtained. After this possibly over-ambitious effort let us turn to a less abstract aspect of computing machines.

We set a machine to play Nim. This was comparatively simple. We have also tried out games of chance on the machine. Games like chess occupy an intermediate position. Chess is not a game of chance and yet one can have good or bad fortune in it. One may make errors or profit by the opponent's errors. In Nim it was only necessary to know the formulae and to calculate correctly. In chess there are no such formulae known at present: it is not even known whether black or white has an advantage or whether correct play always leads to a draw. There are indeed so-called theories of chess but all chess-theory is empirical. Each game of chess is a new problem and this makes it more interesting than Nim, which is completely understood.

## Chess automata

The idea of these is quite old. Philosophers dreamed of automata in the 17th century, while the 18th century inventors built some remarkable constructions in this domain. The most remarkable was a seated Turk, with turban and hookah, who was a good player, able to checkmate most of his human partners. Electronic brains had not been invented at that time – chess still demanded a human brain in those days. In fact the automaton concealed a small man, who directed the Turk's moves.

Even today there is no electronic brain capable of playing chess, and I do not believe it would be worth the cost and labour of constructing one. It is, however, certainly worth considering what one would be like. Internally, of course, since the container would be a box. In the 18th century a chess playing machine would have to look like a chess player; today we do not even demand that an apparatus from which we buy postage stamps should resemble a post-office official.

In the first place the chess machine would contain cells (relays, valves, transistors), which correspond to the 64 squares of the chess board and the 32 pieces. When a piece occupies a square, the cells corresponding to the piece and the square must be somehow connected with one another, as are two telephone subscribers to an exchange. Simultaneously gates are opened, as it were, to certain squares which are commanded by the piece. If one piece bars the way of another, then the gates are shut to all the squares which are no longer accessible. Of course the machine must be told all the rules of the game: castling, capture *en passant*, rules for checkmate and stalemate, draws, and so on.

The result would be a machine of modest dimensions but very complicated structure: an apparent tangle of wires and connections, made with great care. But these are practical problems which can be solved by any technician.

This machine would be able to play chess, that is, it would know the rules, apply them, and protest when the opponent infringed the rules. But otherwise it would be inferior to anyone who has just learnt the rules of chess and is about to play his first game. Any such person would reflect before he made a move, and however clumsy a player, he is still better prepared than the machine, which lacks any organ for reflection and which can at best choose a move at random.

The machine cannot help this. We should have given it

some part where at each stage the best move is worked out. This was done for the Nim-machine and what is fair for one is fair for the other.

Thus we have to design a circuit which works out the best move, or at any rate one which is not too stupid. With Nim it was quite easy to do this: there is an arithmetical rule which defines a good move and the designer has only to translate this rule into the language of switching circuits.

Chess is quite different. Nim has a completely known theory and chess none at all. What is called chess theory consists simply of rules of thumb and traditions, which may all be false. Until the beginning of this century it was believed essential to open with the king's pawn, whereas the queen's pawn is preferred nowadays: perhaps both are wrong and the correct opening is something which has not yet been seriously tried and would be regarded as quite crazy.

No chess theory exists and yet we have to teach it to the machine. This is, of course, impossible. At any rate people play chess, which has no theory, instead of Nim, which has one, and it is precisely the lack of a theory which makes chess enjoyable.

The chess machine would have to imitate human players and reflect. How can it do this? How does a human player?

The human player ponders. He continues the game without moving the pieces. He plays on ahead on an imaginary chess board, where he can take back any move which he doesn't like. He also puts himself in the position of his opponent and makes the latter's moves. He analyses a few alternative continuations, chooses the one which seems best and makes the first move of this continuation.

The machine would have to behave similarly, i.e. play all sorts of alternatives for itself. Suppose it considers ten possible alternative moves at each stage and continues each alternative for ten moves, five of its own and five of its opponent's. This gives $10^{10} = 10,000,000,000$ variations to calculate. If we allow one hundred thousandth of a second for each move this means in one of these calculations reflecting over its next move for a whole day. This is too much.

We wanted the machine to consider ten possibilities in each situation. Could we make do with fewer? But what are we asking? The choice of possible moves is generally much larger and in order to choose only ten of them the machine would have to dispose of some principle for making the selection – a principle which must remain unknown to the opponent, for otherwise it would be easy to lead the machine into a trap. There is yet another difficulty. The machine must naturally keep a record of the variations analysed, so that it can compare them and choose the best one. A magnetic tape can record 100 symbols per square centimeter. If each move requires ten symbols for its description, the $10^{10}$ mentioned above would require a magnetic tape 1 kilometre long and 100 metres wide. But such a memory would be unwieldy.

Even this is not the worst of the difficulties. When the machine has analysed all $10^{10}$ variations, how is it to choose between them? What principle will decide the choice? How does it decide what position is best? If a checkmate occurs among the positions this is a simple matter, but that would be a rare coincidence. The capture of pieces already is a less convincing criterion, especially since the opponent, knowing that the machine hopes for such captures before the 5th move, can dupe the machine with a gambit.

These conclusions are disappointing. We are not able to construct a machine that really plays chess. Yet we know that human players manage to do it, and the question is, how. Our analysis of chess was obviously incomplete. What was left out?

Why need a human player not analyse $10^{10}$ variants before making a move, being content with fewer? The reason is that he has gathered experience in his chess-playing life and has stored it in his memory. Clearly the machine also needs a memory to advise it, whenever necessary.

The human brain is said to contain about $10^{10}$ cells, called neurons. Present-day technology cannot imitate anything on this scale. We saw that $10^{10}$ memory cells would require a magnetic surface of 1 kilometre by 100 metres, which is an impossibility. The cells of the human brain are much more subtle than those of an electronic brain; they are controlled not by valves and transistors, but by molecules, say a protein molecule which attaches itself somewhere to a molecule of riboneucleic acid, or by whatever the exact mechanism is.

The construction of smaller cells and more compact memories is making great progress, but it will be a long time before the technologist overtakes nature. On the other

114

hand he does not have to simulate a whole human brain, but only the surely rather small part with which a man plays chess. The memory capacity of a large modern computer is about that of say, a worm. Obviously this is not yet sufficient to play chess!

Let us be optimistic, however. Suppose this problem is solved and that the machine has an extensive memory. It remembers all the games it has ever played and all the analyses it has carried out during the games and in its spare time. The memory would have to be huge, but let us suppose it so. At each state of the game the machine leafs through its memory and if it finds the state there it uses the notes it made then and chooses its move accordingly.

With this the task of constructing a chess machine appears to be solved, but no, we are as far from the solution as ever. Now we can see the true difficulty. The machine gains nothing by being able to identify its present position with one which has occurred earlier. The probability of meeting the same position twice in one lifetime of chess is extremely small, if one disregards the positions in the traditional openings. The experience which the machine has noted so carefully is of very little use.

The machine has imitated the human chess player badly. The latter does not commit whole games to memory but retains only the essential and discards the inessential. The art of memory includes the art of forgetting.

For example, a beginner who has once experienced that the enemy knight on c7 attacked his king on e8 and his castle on a8 simultaneously, will not easily forget the resulting losses, even although he forgets all the rest of the arrangement of the board. He has learnt something and understands what to do when a similar danger threatens. Our automaton does not understand the idea of 'similar danger'. His highest perception is to recognize complete coincidence of situations. When this position of the knight threatens to occur again in a game, the human player averts it, even when the other pieces on the board are in positions different from those of the first game. The machine can profit from its experiences only when exactly the same situation occurs. The recognition of incomplete agreement, the drawing of analogues, abstractions, the neglect of inessentials and emphasis on the essentials – all this is characteristic of the living intellect. This we forgot in our analysis of the behaviour of the human player. The strength and weakness of present-day machines is that they are set up to recognize equality but not similarity. An automatic cigarette machine is so stupid that it refuses to function when paid with a bank note instead of a coin. A quite different kind of machine would have to be invented, but to this end it would first be necessary to investigate the meaning of similarity, analogy, abstraction, essential, etc.

There are department stores where statistics of the customers entering and leaving are collected. (Incidentally, and inexplicably, more seem to enter than to leave.) In many stores human census takers have been replaced by electronic ones, which observe the customers by means of invisible rays. In smaller businesses and banks there is often a commissionaire to open the door whose task is not only to count but also to greet customers with a 'Good morning' – adding, politely, Sir or Madam as appropriate. If you go to this kind of shop you will observe that these people, although acting almost automatically, hardly ever make a mistake.

Suppose that this faithful retainer dies and that his employer wishes to replace him by an electronic slave. The latter has to count the customers and greet them on entering and leaving – this much is not difficult. But how is it to decide on the addition of the polite Sir or Madam?

The problem is to devise a method of determining at the first glance the sex of customers entering a store. Is there a simple reliable criterion to distinguish the sexes? If I am not mistaken, the machine would have to look at the legs. Women's clothing is extremely varied and it is difficult to discover common features, but fortunately their legs are rather uniformly clad and nylon stockings reflect the light quite differently from men's trousers. Thus female legs can be distinguished roughly from male ones by a machine.

This criterion is good but not good enough. There are also legs without stockings, female legs in other kinds of stockings or in trousers, and various cases where the differences are too small to be of use to a simple machine.

We are stranded when we want to analyse how people themselves distinguish the sexes. We do not know the criteria by which we decide whether a person coming towards us is a man or a woman. In animal psychology rather more is known about these problems. Little birds become very agitated at the sight of a live owl or of a picture showing even vaguely the typical outlines of an owl. The male stickleback reacts to any red object as to an enemy stickleback.

Perhaps our criteria are just as simple as those of animals. One could experiment with photographs and films of parts of the human body by showing them to the subjects of our test and asking whether they were male or female. In this way the most important criteria could be discovered, but if they were too numerous it would be hopeless to teach them to a machine. In this case another method would be preferable. The machine is presented with a large number of people and told whether each is male or female. The machine builds up an archive of pictures, which must be stylised and translated into the machine's language and which it consults and compares with new pictures when necessary. Naturally the machine must be really capable of making a vague comparison of pictures and not only establishing a complete identity of pictures, i.e. be capable of what we called abstraction. The machine must be taught to distinguish the sexes and this education may even have to be continued when it is already working as a commissionaire at the door. The machine is punished when it makes a mistake, it incorporates this experience in its memory and at last a machine will have been educated, which no longer makes mistakes and which determines people's sex at the first glance. The main problem is to teach the machine the art of vague comparison, that is, the formation of abstract notions.

This problem is a deep philosophic one, but of great practical importance. In many places attempts are being made to design machines to read type or even longhand. I can dispense with a typist if a machine can read my writing and so process the manuscript that another machine can set it up in print. How does my secretary manage to decipher my notes in which one 'a' scarcely resembles the next? There is no machine yet which can do this, although there is an urgent need for machines to read cheques, addresses and telephone books. Machines cannot even read typescript and print, because even there, there exist differences between letters which *we* regard as identical, because we can abstract, ignoring the inessential, without being able to say what the inessential is.

The highest accomplishment so far is a machine which can take texts given in the punched hole language and set them in print. All it has to be taught is how to divide up when this is necessary – even this is difficult enough. Machines which translate from one language to another are still in their infancy, although all kinds of people, linguists and mathematicians, are occupied with the problem.

The construction of a machine for distinguishing men from women is not of course an important problem. Such a machine would be comparatively easy to build. The chess machine is a much more difficult case. It would be necessary to teach the machine to make abstractions and no one can explain what exactly this means, although everyone 'knows' what he means by the word. Thus the machine sets us a great philosophical problem because it too would like to learn to make abstractions.

Let us suppose that this problem has been solved. All obstacles have been overcome and a machine has been constructed which can execute and understand the knight's forked attack and all the other abstractions which a good chess player must know. Let us call this machine Caissus. Before his first game he is still a novice. We educate him by playing against him and allotting praise for good play, blame for errors. He proves to be an industrious pupil. When he is left alone, he makes analyses. He has all the time in the world and can devote himself entirely to chess. He neither sleeps nor washes, he doesn't have to clean his teeth, for he has none, he doesn't shave and his nourishment is electric current, which is never turned off. He has a nurse to dust him and a personal physician, the technician. He will soon outstrip his teachers, who can devote only part of their time to the game. To become world champion is a bagatelle for him.

If I am not interested in educating him, I can arrange matters differently. I reflect that it is not good that Caissus should be alone. I build a second machine; a Caissa to be a helpmeet for him. They educate each other by playing together, as twins sometimes do. They know no activity or passion other than the game, since they have not been provided with organs of envy, love or hate.

When we humans play chess, we reflect. Can Caissus and Caissa also THINK?


## Are thinking machines possible?

If by thinking is understood the whole of human intellectual activity, then no. They are extremely narrow specialists, far narrower than the most obsessed humans.

Whatever machines may be built, they will always be specialists who by virtue of their specialisation display superhuman powers in a single domain. The idea of a homunculus is the ideal of a pre-scientific age. To create something which is entirely human there is no need to turn to experts to build an expensive machine. The good old way is still the cheapest and even today, when almost all production is in the hands of specialists, it is just as generally known.

But even restricting oneself to the playing of chess, it can be asked if the activities of Caissus and Caissa deserve the name of thought. 'Why not?' I would reply, 'They are good players and win their games not by magic but by making analyses no different from those of a human player'.

This is a deduction which displeases many people. It is agreeable to imagine that some mysterious process or other accompanies thought. Perhaps this is true and perhaps not. All that I experience when someone else thinks is what he communicates to me as a result, and perhaps some incidental pantomime. The machines provide us with the same (or better) results as the human thinker. If one finds the external symptoms of thought indispensable one can give the machine the appearance of Rodin's thinker, or a forehead to be wrinkled, or shoulders to shrug, according to the requirements of the moment. But this would be ridiculous.

And is the machine conscious of itself? I do not know, because I do not know what this means. If it means memory, then the machine has a high degree of memory. If it means that the machine is capable of saying 'I exist', we simply build in a tape recorder which speaks the magic formula 'I exist' several times daily. Does to be conscious of oneself mean more than this? Perhaps it does, and perhaps it is precisely in the study of machines that we will get to the bottom of it.

The machine can approximate to man in many respects. Man thinks with an end in view, as we know from psychologists. The machine does not, but this too can be built in so that the machine is not only to proceed with systematic analysis but conversely to take a future position and connect it with the existing ones by working backwards. That is working with an end in view; or is there more to it?

Lastly there is the thorny problem of free will, which can be discussed fruitlessly and at great length. What is free will? When do we call a man's decisions free? I believe that is when he does not do exactly what we expect of him, so that we cannot predict his actions with certainty. This is a necessary condition but not yet sufficient. If he is completely unpredictable, if he never acts as I would like, if he turns about like a weathercock, I call him not free, but the slave of his passions – he is not master of himself, but is ruled by them. Summing up, the free man shall be neither too dependent nor too independent of my predictions.

Our machine is not free. It does exactly what I can predict (if I had the time), namely the best move from each position. It should be more human, that is fallible. From time to time it should make a weak move or even break the rules. It should sometimes refuse to play, or even upset the pieces in the middle of play. This ought not to happen too often or at regular intervals. A random device would be necessary to determine the moments for the machine to display its free will. Is this sufficient, or is there more to free will than this?

What if one looks deeper into their brains? We know the contents of the electronic brain and the expert can explain the use of each component. The human brain is very much more complicated. However, a great deal is known in broad outline. It is said to consist, as we have noted, of $10^{10}$ cells, the neurons. These form the great network, the nervous system, which enables man or beast to act appropriately. The circuit elements, the neurons, like relays, vacuum tubes and transistors are, according to present theory, capable of two states, active and neutral; pairs of neurons are connected with a third in such a way that this third neuron reacts on the states of the other two according to the schemes 'and', 'or', 'if . . ., then . . .' and so on. A computer is a marvel but the nervous system is a greater one.

Compared with the human brain the largest computers are small. They will, however, get bigger. Will they reach the size necessary for a logical machine, which can prove all mechanically provable propositions or of a chess machine able to match human players? I hardly think so. The technological problems would be huge.

Then why discuss at such length the capabilities of machines, which exist only in our imagination? Well, numbers and geometric figures, too, exist only in our imagination and yet they have long intrigued men and have become a means of understanding and controlling nature. There are many such means and computing machines are among them: not only the real computers which calculate wages and steer space ships, but also the other ones, which stimulate our thought and lend wings to our fantasy.

# 4 The ABC of life

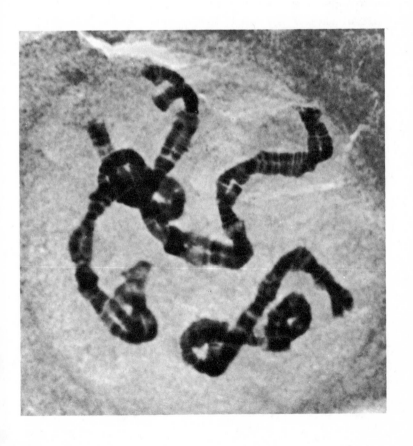

## The genetic code

As soon as, in fertilisation, the spermatozoon and ovum have united, all the inherited and hereditary qualities of the new creature are determined. A blueprint is traced out in the microscopically small world of the cell, and it is copied at each division of the cell so that each cell knows what its job as part of the whole is. In this blueprint all the qualities are listed which the creature has in common with its fellows, and all those in which it differs from them: that I am a human being and not an anemone, an amoeba, a butterfly, a reptile or a cat is written in it; so too is the way in which my muscles, my liver and my kidneys should function; that I should see and speak, what colour my skin, my hair and my eyes will have; whether I am a man or a woman, whether right-handed or left-handed, whether colour blind, whether diabetic, in fact my whole physical and spiritual constitution.

The variety of proteins (types of albumen) underlies the variety of living nature. Proteins are long chains (actually double chains) of amino acids. An amino acid is obtained if one of the H atoms (not the one in the OH group) in a fatty acid

is replaced by an amino radical $NH_2$. Such an amino acid

behaves at the COOH end like an acid, at the NH$_2$ end like a base. In this way, the amino acids can be joined together in long chains, and this produces the proteins, from hundreds or hundreds of thousands of amino acids.

One can imagine millions of different amino acids. Twenty are distinguished as being the building blocks of the proteins, the same twenty for the whole of living nature, from the bacterium to homo sapiens. This is fortunate, since it is for this reason that we can live from our fellow creatures. Plants alone are able to build up amino acids – from air and light. We derive our amino acids from plants, directly if we are vegetarians and indirectly with a carnivorous diet. We have to synthesize our proteins from the amino acids. These acids, in varying number and order, are arranged in a row to form protein chains: long words, so to speak, built up from twenty letters. The structure of some, the quite short ones, is known exactly; for example that of insulin, which plays an important role in the decomposition of carbohydrates – it happens that some types of mammal have differently constructed insulins. With the longer proteins, even individuals of the same species differ.

The inherited blueprint which says how the new creature has to build up its proteins is found in the fertilised cell in the so-called chromosomes (forty-six in humans), which under closer examination fall into thousands of pieces, small disks each corresponding to a hereditary characteristic. These are the deoxyribonucleic acids, whose structure was clarified a few years ago by Watson and Crick. They too are chains consisting of few bricks, two pyrimidines, thymine and cytosine, and two purines, adenine and guanine, which follow one another in such a deoxyibonucleic acid in various orders: each chain is a long word so to speak, which is built up of four letters.

It is the ribonucleic acids which carry out the synthesis of proteins. (I leave out the prefix 'deoxy' here once and for all; before the deoxyribonucleic acids work at building up protein, they are subjected to one more transformation.)

The hereditary information, which is stored up in the ribonucleic acids, is now transmitted in two ways. First it is copied at each cell division; secondly it is translated from the four letter alphabet of the ribonucleic acids into the twenty letter alphabet of the proteins during protein synthesis. In fact there are living organisms which can only manage the first: viruses, which consist almost completely of ribonucleic acid and multiply in guest cells with the material that is there.

Nature has devised an ingenious method for the copying. Ribonucleic acids are actually double chains, which are related to each other like the positive and negative of a photograph. A guanine is always opposite a cytosine and vice versa, and an adenine is opposite a thymine and vice versa. If the ribonucleic acid is to be copied, the double chain splits along its length, and now each single chain is completed to a double chain once more; each positive builds up its negative, and each negative its positive.

The second activity is more complicated: to translate from the four letter alphabet of the ribonucleic acids into the twenty letter alphabet of the proteins. This must happen according to a code, and biochemists are now working on the problem of deciphering this code.

Is it then at all possible to write all information expressible with twenty letters also with four letters? Naturally, we can render everything written with the twenty-six letters of our ordinary alphabet by means of the Morse dot-dash signals; to be more precise I should say: dot, dash and space, since without a space I would not know where the dot-dash combination which represents a letter, started or stopped.

The genetic code might be a space-free code. Are there indeed such codes, and how can they be constructed?

## Space-free codes

Let us call the letters of the ribonucleic-acid alphabet $a$, $b$, $c$, $d$. We call an ordered pair of these letters, as for example $ab$, $dc$, $cc$, a digram; an ordered triplet such as for example $cda$, $bbc$, $aaa$, a trigram. We will attempt the construction with the trigrams. Let us assume that a trigram corresponds to each of the twenty letters $a$, $\beta$, $\gamma$, ... of the protein alphabet – three ribonucleic components juxtaposed in a definite order are thus necessary to attract a given one of the twenty amino acids and to put it into the right place in the protein chain which has to be built. We then have a code like, for example,

$$abc = \alpha$$
$$dda = \beta$$
$$cbd = \gamma$$
$$bda = \delta$$
etc.

It is a pity that this would be unsuitable. A ribonucleic-acid word like

$$abcbdabdaddacbdabcbda$$

would be translated into protein writing as

$$a\,\delta\,\delta\,\beta\,\gamma\,a\,\delta.$$

If we consider the fourteenth, fifteenth and sixteenth letters of the first word, however, we see that a *bda* has been formed by the juxtaposition of $\gamma = cbd$ and $a = abc$, and this should correspond to $\delta$. This trigram could attract an amino acid $\delta$ in protein synthesis and disturb the whole synthesis, as does a piece which does not fit into a jig-saw puzzle. The requirement that a code be space free is something that cannot be easily satisfied. This produces a mathematical problem. How should we formulate it?

Altogether $4^3 = 64$ trigrams can be formed from four letters $a$, $b$, $c$, $d$. Twenty such trigrams – a system $S$ – are now to be selected so that if $xyz$ and $uvw$ belong to the system $S$, neither $yzu$ nor $zuv$ are allowed to belong to the system $S$. ($x$, $y$, $z$, $u$, $v$, $w$ are here variables for which $a$, $b$, $c$, $d$ can be substituted.) Is there such a system $S$?

We note first of all that if $xyz$ is in $S$, then $yzx$ and $zxy$ must not be in $S$. In particular, the trigrams $aaa$, $bbb$, $ccc$, $ddd$ are forbidden. In the remaining $64 - 4$ only one out of each triplet of trigrams $xyz$, $yzx$, $zxy$ is allowed. The condition that the code be space free thus has as consequence that $S$ can consist of at most twenty trigrams. The appearance here again of the number twenty is a hopeful sign.

We again formulate the mathematical problem whose solution should occupy us.

## Solution of a problem

*Problem*: Let a trigram be understood to mean an ordered triplet, which is formed out of the letters $a$, $b$, $c$, $d$. Let a system $S$ of trigrams be called a code if

$$xyz \text{ in } S \text{ and } uvw \text{ in } S$$

implies

$$yzu \text{ is not in } S \text{ and } zuv \text{ is not in } S.$$

All codes with the maximum number (20) of trigrams are to be found.

We now assume that we have such a code $S$ and consider the following:

1 Exactly one of the triplets $xyz$, $yzx$, $zxy$ belongs to $S$, except when $x = y = z$ (in that case, none does).

That at most one belongs to $S$ follows directly from the requirement that the code be space free. Since there are only twenty such triplets of trigrams, one trigram from each triplet must in fact be represented in $S$, for $S$ should indeed contain twenty trigrams.

2 We understand by $S_x$ the totality of trigrams of $S$ in which $x$ stands in the middle; by $L_x$ and $R_x$, the totality of letters which occur in $S_x$ as left or right neighbour of $x$ respectively.

3 If $u$ is in $L_x$ and $v$ is in $R_x$ and $u$, $v$ are not both equal to $x$, then $uxv$ is in $S$.

For by assumption there are certain

$$qxv \text{ in } S \text{ and } uxp \text{ in } S.$$

From this it follows that

$$xvu \text{ is not in } S \text{ and } vux \text{ is not in } S;$$

thus by 1

$$uxv \text{ is in } S,$$

which we wanted to prove.

4 We introduce an abbreviated description of the set $S_x$: we write $x$ four times in the middle column, the members of $L_x$ in the left column, and those of $R_x$ in the right column. Thus, for example, if $L_b$ consists of $a$, $b$, $d$ and $R_b$ of $b$ and $c$, we write

$$\begin{array}{cl} & ab \\ S_b: & bbb \\ & bc \\ & db \end{array}$$

This is to be read as follows: to obtain $S_b$, we may combine $b$ as middle member with each member of the left column on the left and each member of the right column on the right; only $bbb$ is forbidden.

5 If $x$ is neither in $L_x$ nor in $R_x$, then $S_x$ is empty (contains no trigram).

Suppose $x$ is not in $L_x$ and also not in $R_x$, and that $uxv$ for example is in $S$, with $u \neq x$, say. Then $uxx$ and $xxu$ are not in $S$; thus by 2 $xux$ is certainly in $S$. This contradicts, however, the assumption that $uxv$ was in $S$.

6 No digram *pq* can occur both on the left and on the right in *S*.

We assume that

6·0           *pqx* is in *S* and *ypq* is in *S*.

If there were a trigram in *S* ending with *y*, say *uvy*, this would lead together with *pqx* to the contradiction that *ypq* may not be in *S*. Thus there is no trigram in *S* ending with *y*. Similarly, it can be shown that there is no trigram in *S* starting with *x*. This implies that

$$x \neq y.$$

Further, for each *z*,

         *xxz* is not in *S* and *xzx* is not in *S*.

Thus, by 1 for $z \neq x$

6·1           *zxx* is in *S*.

Similarly,

         *zyy* is not in *S* and *yzy* is not in *S*.

Thus, by 1 for $z \neq y$

6·2           *yyz* is in *S*.

In particular, 6·1−2 with *y* and *x* respectively instead of *z* imply

6·3           *yxx* is in *S*,
6·4           *yyx* is in *S*.

6·1 and 6·4 imply

6·5               $yxz$ is not in $S$ for $z \neq x$;

6·3 and 6·2 imply

6·6               $zyx$ is not in $S$ for $z \neq y$.

Because of 1, 6·5–6 imply

$xzy$ is in $S$ for each $z \neq x$, $z \neq y$,

but this contradicts the result that no trigram can start with $x$ or end with $y$.

Thus our assumption 6·0 was false, and our statement is thereby proved.

7 $x$ cannot occur in both $L_x$ and $R_x$,

For otherwise one would then have the digram $xx$ both on the left and on the right.

An $S_b$ such as we gave as example in 4 is thus impossible.

8 If $x$ is in $R_x$ and $u$ is in $R_x$ ($u \neq x$), then $u$ is also in $L_x$.

By assumption $xx$ and $xu$ occur as digrams on the right in $S$. By 6 they cannot also occur as digrams on the left. Thus

$xxu$ is not in $S$ and $xux$ is not in $S$.

Hence by 1

$uxx$ is in $S$,

i.e. $u$ is indeed in $L_x$.

9 Let $S_x$ be non-empty. By 5 $x$ must then be a member

either of $R_x$ or of $L_x$. We wish to assume for the moment that $x$ is in $R_x$. The number of members of $S_x$, $R_x$, $L_x$ shall be called $s_x$, $r_x$, $l_x$, respectively. $3 \cdot 8$ implies

$$r_x \leqslant l_x + 1.$$

By 3

$$s_x = l_x \cdot r_x.$$

Let the number of trigrams in $S_x$ with two equal letters be called $s^1 x$. Then

$$s'_x = l_x + r_x - 1.$$

There are at most the following possibilities if $x$ is in $R_x$:

| $r_x =$ | 4 | 3 | 2 | 1 | 3 | 2 | 1 | 2 | 1 | 0 |
|---|---|---|---|---|---|---|---|---|---|---|
| $l_x =$ | 3 | 3 | 3 | 3 | 2 | 2 | 2 | 1 | 1 | 0 |
| $s_x =$ | 12 | 9 | 6 | 3 | 6 | 4 | 2 | 2 | 1 | 0 |
| $s'_x =$ | 6 | 5 | 4 | 3 | 4 | 3 | 2 | 2 | 1 | 0 |

(the case of an empty $S_x$ is added with the zeros in the last column).

$S$ should have exactly twenty trigrams and among them exactly twelve with two identical letters occur. Thus

$$s_a + s_b + s_c + s_d = 20,$$
$$s'_a + s'_b + s'_c + s'_d = 12.$$

Taking this into account in the above list, we get for the four numbers

$$s_d, \ s_c, \ s_b, \ s_a$$

only the possibilities

|      |     |    |    |   |
|------|-----|----|----|---|
| I    | 12, | 6  | 2, | 0 |
| II   | 12, | 6, | 1, | 1 |
| III  | 12, | 4, | 4, | 0 |
| IV   | 9,  | 9, | 2, | 0 |
| V    | 9,  | 9, | 1, | 1 |

and, of course, everything which arises from interchanging the letters $a, b, c, d$.

$$s_d = 12.$$

For $S_d$, we only have

$$ada$$
$$bdb$$
$$cdc$$
$$dd$$

and what arises from it by interchanging right and left. In this $S_d$, the diagrams $ad$, $bd$, $cd$ occur on the left; by 6 they cannot occur on the right anywhere else. Thus $d$ (apart from in $S_d$) cannot occur anywhere else as right-hand member of a trigram of $S$. Moreover, the diagrams $da$, $db$, $dc$ occur on the right in $S_d$, and thus cannot occur anymore on the left. Thus $d$ also cannot occur as left-hand member of a trigram of $S$. Consequently, $d$ does not occur in $S$ at all outside $S_d$.

$$s_c = 6.$$

For $S_c$ we only have

$$aca$$
$$bcb$$
$$cc$$
$$c \ ,$$

possibly with left and right interchanged. As just above, we further conclude that $c$ cannot occur in $S_b$ and $S_a$ anymore. In case I with $s_b = 2$, $S_b$ is necessarily

$$aba$$
$$bb$$
$$b$$
$$b$$

up to possible interchange of right and left and empty $S_a$. In case II with $s_b = s_a = 1$, $S_b$ and $S_a$ are

| | |
|---|---|
| $ab$ | $aa$ |
| $bb$ | $ba$ |
| $b$ | $a$ |
| $b$ | $a$ |

where again right and left may be interchanged, but then only simultaneously in $S_b$ and in $S_a$, since otherwise the digram $ab$, for example, would occur on the left and right.

### $s_c = 4$.

We may assume that $c$ is in $R_c$, up to interchange of right and left. If $b$ is in $R_c$, by 8 $b$ is in $L_c$, too. Then $cb$ may no longer appear on the left as a digram and $bc$ may no longer appear on the right, i.e. $c$ may no longer be a neighbour of $b$. Only $a$ and $b$ remain as neighbours of $b$, and that would give at most two for $s_b$, while in III we should have $s_b = 4$. Thus $b$ is not in $R_c$, and we get

| | |
|---|---|
| $aca$ | $aba$ |
| $bc$ | $bb$ |
| $cc$ | $cb$ |
| $c$ | $b$ |

again with the possibility of simultaneous interchange of right and left.

$$s_d = s_c = 9.$$

We assume $d$ is in $R_d$. If $c$ were in $R_d$, by 8 it would also be in $L_d$. As above, we then see that $d$ occurs neither on the left nor on the right in $S_c$. Since $c$ only occurs either in $L_c$ or in $R_c$, $s_c \leq 6$, while we should have $s_c = 9$. For this reason, $c$ cannot be in $R_d$. Thus $S_d$ and similarly $S_c$ are

| | |
|---|---|
| *ada* | *aca* |
| *bdb* | *bcb* |
| *cd* | *cc* |
| *dd* | *dc* |

again with possible simultaneous interchange of right and left. *ad, bd, ac, bc* can now no longer occur on the right, similarly *da, db, ca, cb* cannot occur on the left anymore. Thus $c$ and $d$ do not occur anymore at all. Hence, for $s_b = 2$, $s_a = 0$ we have

*aba*
*bb*
*b*
*b* ,

for $s_b = s_a = 1$

| | |
|---|---|
| *ab* | *aa* |
| *bb* | *ba* |
| *b* | *a* |
| *b* | *a* , |

again with the usual possibility of interchanging sides.

10 We put the result together. The complete solution of the problem is given by:

| I | | | | |
|---|---|---|---|---|
| | *ada* | *aca* | *aba* | *a* |
| | *bdb* | *bcb* | *bb* | *a* |
| | *cdc* | *cc* | *b* | *a* |
| | *dd* | *c* | *b* | *a* |
| II | | | | |
| | *ada* | *aca* | *ab* | *aa* |
| | *bdb* | *bcb* | *bb* | *ba* |
| | *cdc* | *cc* | *b* | *a* |
| | *dd* | *c* | *b* | *a* |
| III | | | | |
| | *ada* | *aca* | *aba* | *a* |
| | *bdb* | *bc* | *bb* | *a* |
| | *cdc* | *cc* | *cb* | *a* |
| | *dd* | *c* | *b* | *a* |
| IV | | | | |
| | *ada* | *aca* | *aba* | *a* |
| | *bdb* | *bcb* | *bb* | *a* |
| | *cd* | *cc* | *b* | *a* |
| | *dd* | *dc* | *b* | *a* |
| V | | | | |
| | *ada* | *aca* | *ab* | *aa* |
| | *bdb* | *bcb* | *bb* | *ba* |
| | *cd* | *cc* | *b* | *a* |
| | *dd* | *dc* | *b* | *a* |

In this we may further

1 interchange the letters *a*, *b*, *c*, *d* at will,

2 interchange right and left in each block $S_x$;

however, the interchange in the following pairs of blocks can only be done simultaneously: in the third and the fourth of II, in the second and third of III, in the first and second of IV, in the first and second as well as in the third and fourth of V. By this means

I, II decompose into eight types

III, IV, V decompose into four types.

Interchanges of the letters $a$, $b$, $c$, $d$ apart, there are twenty-eight solutions.

11 We have only shown up to now that at most the specified systems solve the problem. It is still necessary to check that they all really do it. However, this is so easy that we can pass over it.


### Conclusions

Is one of the twenty-eight stated really the ABC of life? Nature, not the mathematician, is qualified to answer this question. By means of experiment we put questions to it, and if the questions are sensible, it gives sensible answers.

The simplicity of the results could inspire confidence in us. However, the results are so simple only because we started from simple hypotheses. Is nature really as simple as that?

Now, it has appeared in the meantime that things are more complicated. It would have been too good to be true. But this does not matter. We have amused ourselves with the solution of a pretty mathematical problem, and to amuse oneself also belongs to the ABC of life.

# 5 The art of drawing badly

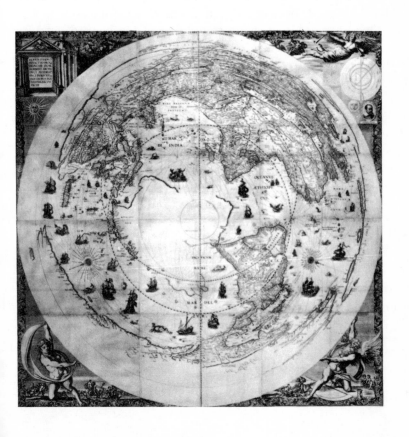

## Distorting letters

Once having learnt to read, we would never mistake an X for a U. In this chapter, however, we shall have to forget a lot of things we were first taught at school. A J, for example, if straightened out becomes an I. If I exert myself a bit more, I can achieve the same with a C and U, indeed also with an S. One only needs to swing round one of the parts of an L or V, to turn it into an I. I, if bent twice, becomes a Z or an N, and if bent three times, M or W.

All the following figures

$$C, I, J, L, M, N, S, U, V, W, Z \qquad (1)$$

are, as one says, topologically equivalent. They can be laid one on top of the other – not as congruent triangles can, by a displacement of one into the other, nor in the sense of similarity, after they have been magnified or shrunk; nor by a projection such as maps a circle into an ellipse, for example. These figures can only be laid on each other after they have been continuously deformed.

This would not work with an O. If we wanted to place it on an I, we would first have to cut it open, which we do not allow, or would have to squash the O flat so that points different on the O coincide on the I, which we equally forbid. O is not topologically equivalent to I, nor is it topologically equivalent to any of the other figures in the set (1). On the other hand,

$$D, O \qquad (2)$$

are topologically equivalent to each other. Of yet another

topological type are

$$E, F, G, T, Y \tag{3}$$

which are certainly topologically equivalent to each other:
one has only to rotate the upper and lower transverse lines
of the E upwards and downwards respectively and the whole
figure through 90° to the right in order to obtain a T after
some shortening and lengthening of the components. The
case of F is somewhat simpler. If one keeps the horizontal
transverse line of the G fixed and pulls the curved piece
straight, something like a T results. With the Y one only
needs slightly to lower the oblique parts to get the same
thing. At no point of these transformations have I cut
through anything that was joined or joined together anything
that was separated – all this was explicitly forbidden. For
this reason I also cannot alter any of the figures (3) into
figures (1) or (2). T and its topological equivalents are
distinguished by a point from which three arms radiate –
something that never occurs in (1) or (2). This is still not all,
however. In

$$K, X \tag{4}$$

four arms radiate from one definite point, and for this
reason they are topologically different to (1), (2), (3), although
they are equivalent to each other. In

$$H \tag{5}$$

there are two points with three arms; it forms a type by
itself. In

$$P \tag{6}$$

a closed curve is included, as in (2). Topologically speaking, it is a circle on one foot, and in this way it is different from (2).

$$Q, R \qquad\qquad (7)$$

can both be regarded as a circle with two feet which radiate from the same point,

$$A \qquad\qquad (8)$$

as a circle with two feet which start from different points. There still remains

$$B \qquad\qquad (9)$$

two circles, which are stuck together at a point.


## Geometry and topology

Geometry means measurement of the earth, and although people soon learnt to make abstractions from the earth, yet for two and a half millennia the geometer was still concerned with measurement. Then, however, geometries appeared which dealt only with points, straight lines and planes, but no longer with distances and angles which were to be measured. The ruler's edge was in fact still used in them, but the division into inches on its longer side was not used anymore. Gradually geometers appeared, becoming numerous in our century, who abandoned the ruler, poor drawers to whom a curve like figure 5·1 was worth just as much as a straight line segment, a closed curve like figure 5·2 just as much as a circle. This branch of geometry is called *topology*.

**Figure 5·1**   **Figure 5·2**

## Maps

The game we played just now with Roman letters was topology of curves. Let us now proceed to surfaces.

The prototype surface is of course the sphere. But wait a moment, that was a hasty remark. For a long time men thought they lived on a circular disk. The circle is indeed the most beautiful figure that can be drawn in the plane if one wants to construct a map. It is not quite so easy to make a map of a closed earth's surface. We already mentioned in chapter 1 how this is done. The earth is divided along the equator into northern and southern hemispheres, or along the zero meridian into east and west hemispheres. These are both mapped into the plane as circular disks and laid side by side. The points of the equator or the zero meridian are then mapped twice as boundary points of the circular disks. Signs on the boundary indicate how the boundaries are to be identified with each other. This is a model of the spherical surface. In Mercator maps the earth is mapped on to a rectangle; the whole upper edge counts as the North pole, the lower one as the South pole, and points at the same latitude on the left and right edges are to be identified with

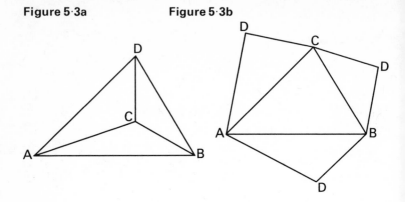

Figure 5·3a         Figure 5·3b

each other. If we wish to construct in the plane a model of a tetrahedron, which is also a closed surface, we place it with one side on the plane and fold down the three other sides on to the same plane (figure 5·3). We get a form of hexagon with easily visible identifications on the edge. Finally, we can make a whole atlas of a surface with detailed maps of the neighbourhoods of its points; all kinds of signs such as place names, rivers, lakes, degrees of latitude and longitude show how the various pages of the map are to be wholly or partially identified with each other.

## Examples of surfaces

When the earth's surface ceased to be a circular disk, it had to be a spherical surface, since that is the most beautiful closed surface. From a topological point of view, most of the solids which we deal with are indeed also spheres, our own body not excluded. In the invisibly small world even, we still visualise electrons, protons and light quanta as small spheres.

Yet there is a mischief-maker even among our neighbours in the universe, namely Saturn's ring. Let a man on Saturn's ring draw a map of his world. He divides the ring he lives

**Figure 5·4a**                                        145

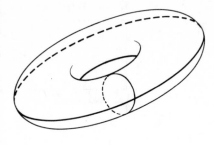

**Figure 5·4b**

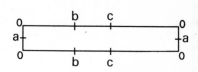

on along a meridian. This is still not enough, however. A cylinder results and in order to lay it in the plane, it must be cut again, in fact along a generator, i.e. along a circle of latitude of the ring (figure 5·4). The map then has the form of a rectangle, with curious identifications. Points on the right and left at the same latitude on Saturn's ring are to be identified, just as are points at the top and bottom at the same longitude on Saturn's ring.

Mathematically, such a surface is called a torus. A torus is really something different from a spherical surface. On the torus, we can construct for example, an ocean and with it an island, a continent with two separated shores both of which are closed curves. See figure 5·5 where the island is hatched and the unhatched part is the – connected – ocean. On the sphere this sort of thing is not possible. An island in the ocean with a lake in the middle has in fact two shores, but there the mass of water is not connected.

Matters become still more complicated on the surface of a ladder with $p + 1$ rungs, if $p > 1$. (For $p = 0$ and $p = 1$ we get ladders with 1 or 2 rungs, but these are nothing else topologically than sphere and torus with several, topologically unimportant protuberances.) This again is some-

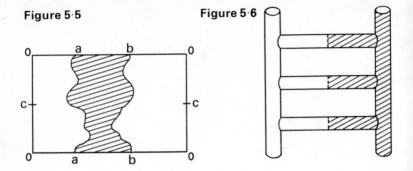

**Figure 5·5**  **Figure 5·6**

thing new. On such a surface there are islands in the ocean with $p + 1$ separated coasts. In this connection see figure 5·6 where the left half represents the ocean, the right the mainland, and where the coast consists of $p + 1$ circles.

In topology, such a surface is said to be of genus $p$; the sphere's surface is of genus 0, the torus of genus 1.

A surface of genus $p$ can be represented as follows:

Bore $p$ canals through a solid sphere so that they pierce it and do not meet each other. The outer surface of the remaining solid is then, as can be seen, of genus $p$. Thus the human body gives a surface of really high genus, if we not only pay attention to the outer skin surface but also include the surfaces of the mucous membranes of the alimentary canal and digestive tract and the surfaces of other canals. Still further physical bodies can be quoted which are not bounded by a spherical surface.

One can imagine still more closed surfaces. One of them is the so-called *projective plane*. In the ordinary plane, there are line pairs which intersect, and others, parallels, which do not have a point of intersection. In various investigations more unity is agreeable. We then complete the plane with ideal points or points at infinity. *One* point at infinity should lie on each straight line and in fact the same one on each family of parallel straight lines. The horizontal straight lines

**Figure 5·7**     **Figure 5·8**     147

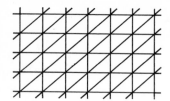

in figure 5·7 have the same point at infinity, all the oblique ones have the same point at infinity, but it is different from the one of the horizontal lines; the vertical lines have a third, etc. All points at infinity lie on a straight line, the line at infinity. According to this stipulation each two distinct straight lines have exactly one point of intersection: non-parallel lines have a finite one, as their points at infinity are of course different; parallel straight lines intersect in a point at infinity, and similarly, the line at infinity intersects each finite line in a point at infinity. The straight lines of the projective plane are closed. If one moves along such a straight line to infinity, one returns through infinity from the other side (figure 5·8).

This is the projective plane. We deform it slightly so as to construct a map of it. We push the line at infinity into the finite region, as the horizon so to speak of the field of view. On this horizon, however, diametric points must be identified; if one goes towards the horizon on one side, one should indeed return from the other. This produces the map of figure 5·9, a circular disk with diametric identification on the rim. It is quite a remarkable form of identification. It cannot be realised with glue or the sewing machine. But in the abstract it is unassailable.

The projective plane is completely different from the

## Figure 5·9    Figure 5·10

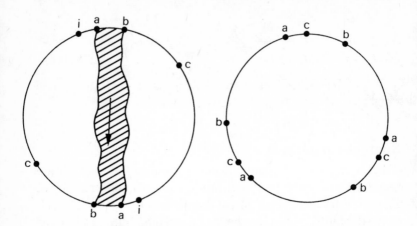

earlier surfaces. It is closed, but in a different way from the previous ones. Let us draw a narrow river (hatched) in this world. It has only one bank. The world traveller, who sets sail on the river from *a* (top), has the lighthouse *i* at *a* on his starboard. When he again arrives at *a* (bottom) the same lighthouse *i* is on his port side. Those who stayed at home and meet him in the harbour will, however, find out to their surprise that he has become left-handed from the exertions of his journey, that his heart now beats on his right, that the hands of his pocket-watch turn anticlockwise and that the screws of the ship's portholes get tighter when someone who remained at home tries to unscrew them. The world traveller has to sail round the world once more if he wants to restore the old state of affairs.

Surfaces on which such strange things can happen are called non-orientable. The projective plane is not the only non-orientable surface.

Any one of the orientable surfaces we have enumerated has a non-orientable counterpart.

We only mention this in passing and turn to a new question: what in fact do we call a surface?

## Surfaces in general

The answer has already been indicated in the above: something of which I can make a (plane) map in the neighbourhood of each of its points.

It is a good idea to make this clear with examples of non-surfaces. A sphere with a small tail, which is to be regarded as a curve, is no longer a surface: I should otherwise have to provide a map containing the small tail's point of attachment with a similar continuation, but this can no longer be called a map. Two spheres glued together at a point do not form a surface either, or, given a pair of normal maps, one would have to identify a point on one of them with another point, without their neighbourhoods joining in (like two pages of an atlas stuck together by a blob of jam: such a mess is not a proper map). Naturally, the two spheres may not be glued together along a line or part of their surfaces either, if a surface is required, since the neighbourhood of the glued line or of the edge of the glued surface no longer has the character of a map. The following example is similar (figure 5·10): identify points on the circumference of the circular disk whose angular coordinates differ by 120° or 240°; thus there are always exactly three points of the circumference which are identified with each other. The result is not a surface either; the curve *abc* has three banks on the surface instead of the two which occur on a map.

A surface should be an atlas of maps with definite identifications. It should be possible to represent the neighbourhood of each point itself again as a map. Hence, it is reasonable to require that each point occur as an interior point on at least one map: its neighbourhood can then be taken in at a glance. If a point appears on several maps, its neighbourhoods, originating from the different maps, should be identified by virtue of the prescribed identification. (If an interior point of one map appears as a boundary point on another, the neighbourhoods' identification naturally only takes place partially.) Interior points of the same map should naturally never be identified with each other, since that could disturb the cartographic character of their neighbourhood.

Finally, we must impose one more condition. A surface should indeed be connected and not consist of say two separated spherical surfaces. How does this appear in an atlas? Start with map no. 1. Points can occur on it which also appear on, say, maps no. 3, no. 7, no. 11. There are points on map no. 3 which lie also on map 1, map 11, map 12; points from maps 1, 12, 14 on map 7; points from maps 1, 3, 14, 19 on map 11. In short, maps 3, 7, 11 join on to map 1, maps 1, 11, 12 join on to map 3, maps 1, 12, 14 join on to map 7, and so on. If we now continue in this way, we should finally be able to reach each map of the atlas – this is the condition which we must still impose.

An atlas can consist of infinitely many maps. At the same time it it can be that infinitely many maps are really needed, as for example with the surface of a ladder with infinitely many rungs. If there is an adequate atlas containing only a finite number of maps, the surface is called *closed*.

## Manifolds

The above contains a precise definition of what the topologist calls a surface and, in particular, a closed surface. We could bring this definition to a more compact form, but instead of this we will turn our attention to yet higher dimensions.

We encountered a certain closed space in chapter 1. We took two solid spheres and identified their surfaces. If one were to travel in such a space, having arrived at the edge of one sphere one would automatically come to the other one. There are no boundaries in this space.

If we wish to describe such spaces by the means known to us in connection with surfaces, we must replace the plane maps by something in three dimensions, say, globes or cubes, and compose an atlas from them. Moreover, the conditions imposed on such an atlas are the same as those for the atlas of a surface. The resulting object is called a *manifold* by topologists. The closed space from chapter 1 is an example of a manifold (admittedly, for this case we must extend the atlas somewhat so that each point appears as interior point of some 'map').

Another example: take a solid sphere, cut out of it a concentric, smaller solid sphere and then identify the inner surface of the remaining spherical shell with its outer surface. This can for example happen in such a way that

Figure 5·11                    Figure 5·12

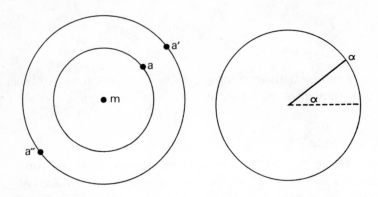

two identified points lie in the same (or the opposite) direction from the centre: in figure 5·11, $a$ and $a'$ or $a$ and $a''$ respectively. It can be shown that these two identifications lead to fundamentally different manifolds.

## Mappings of a circle

Another example (5·12) may further illustrate topology.

We take a circle $C$ and map it into itself, i.e. we associate with each point of $C$ a point of $C$, which we call its image. We can denote a point of $C$ by the angle $a$ which the line joining it to the centre makes with a fixed direction. Of course, in calculations involving these angles, we must always work up to multiples of 360°.

The mapping which maps each point $a$ on to itself is called the identity mapping. The mapping which carries $a$ on to $a + 10°$ (for each $a$) is less trivial. It is a rotation of the circle through 10°. Something completely different is the mapping which carries each point $a$ on to twice itself, $2a$, thus 0° on to 0°, 30° on to 60°, 180° on to 0°, and so on. In contrast to the previous ones, this mapping is no longer 'one-to-one', but 'two-to-one'; there are pairs of points with the same image, while under the first mappings different points also had different images. The mapping which maps each $a$ on to its triple $3a$ is three-to-one; points whose angles differ by $120°$ or $240°$ are mapped on to the same point. For each integer $n$, we can consider the mapping which carries $a$ on to $na$. $n$ must indeed be integral here. $\frac{1}{2}$ for example would not be permissible, since $0°$ and $360°$, which represent the same point, should also have the same image, while $\frac{1}{2} \cdot 0°$ and $\frac{1}{2} \cdot 360° = 180°$ are in fact different points. It is not forbidden to take $n$ (integral and) negative. For $n = -1$ we get the mapping which carries $a$ on to $-a$ for all $a$. This is a reflection of the circle $C$ in a diameter. It is again a one-to-one mapping. For $n = -2$ we again get a two-to-one mapping of $C$, but yet different to the one for $n = 2$. Similarly for any integer $n$. If $a$ describes the circle $C$ once, the image $na$ describes it $n$ times; $-na$ does the same, but in the opposite direction. If we imagine $C$ as a rubber band which is put round a wooden disk, it is stretched $n$ times round the disk after the mapping, in the same or reversed direction. Furthermore, $n = 0$ is also permissible. The whole of $C$ is then mapped on to the single point $0°$.

This naturally does not exhaust all the mappings of $C$ into itself. The rubber band can also be laid round the wooden disk with its tension varying from place to place. One can even introduce folds. But on no account do we want to tear it. This is expressed mathematically as follows: the mapping to be *continuous*; adjacent points to remain adjacent.

**Figure 5·13**          **Figure 5·14**

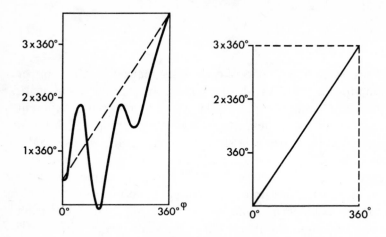

We can represent such a mapping, which we will call $f$, graphically (figure 5·13). Angles from 0° to 360° are marked off on the horizontal axis. It is suitable, as we shall soon see, to work quite calmly with images of more than 360° and less than 0°. If $a$ has the image $f(a)$ we erect a perpendicular on the horizontal axis with length $f(a)$ (negative lengths downwards) and mark the end of the perpendicular. We start this process at 0° and continue it so that the ends of the perpendiculars lie on a curve. If the perpendicular attains the length 360°, we do not jump back to 0°, but continuously extend the lengths of the perpendiculars, possibly beyond 360°. If in doing this we hit 720°, we continue there analogously, and similarly if we reach 0° we plot negative values.

The mapping is thus reproduced graphically by an unbroken curve. In this connection, note that for $f(0°)$ and $f(360°)$ to represent the same point of $C$, they must be equal up to a multiple $p . 360°$ of 360°. (In figure, $p = 3$.) Earlier we discussed mappings $f$, which are defined by

$$f(a) = na \qquad (n \text{ integral}).$$

Such a mapping is reproduced graphically by a straight line (see figure 5·14, where $n = 3$; for negative, $n$, the straight line would descend obliquely, for $n = 0$ it would be horizontal). These mappings are, in contrast to mappings such as those in figure 5·13, without folds; it is easily seen that folds of the mappings $f$ correspond to the rising and falling of the curve in figure 5·13.

## Degree of a mapping

We wish to classify in some way the mappings of the circle $C$ into itself. We place two mappings into the same class if they can be continuously transformed into each other, i.e. if one of them can be produced from the other by continuous modification. This classification principle, which stems from the Dutch mathematician L. E. J. Brouwer (about 1910), has proved to be immensely fruitful in topology. Indeed the modern development of topology really starts with it.

Continuous modification of the graphical representation corresponds also to continuous change of a mapping. Only, care must be taken that in modifying the graphical representation 0° and 360° always have the same image; thus $f(0°)$ and $f(360°)$ may only be moved an equal amount upwards and downwards.

We saw before that some relation

$$f(360°) = f(0°) + n . 360°$$

exists between the angular coordinates of $f(0°)$ and $f(360°)$. The integer $n$ is called the degree of the mapping $f$. The mapping defined earlier by

$$g(a) = na$$

thus has degree $n$.

If $f$ is continuously modified, $f(0°)$ and $f(360°)$ change by the same amount. The degree of a mapping thus remains the same under continuous modifications.

If the mappings $f_0$ and $f_1$ have the same degree $n$, they can be continuously transformed into each other in the following way: for each $a$ let the value $f_0(a)$ move uniformly to $f_1(a)$ in the time interval from 0 to 1, so that at time $t$ it is

$$f_t(a) = (1 - t)f_0(a) + tf_1(a).$$

The transformation of $f_0$ into $f_1$ occurs via $f_t$ $(0 < t < 1)$. Under it, we have

$$\begin{aligned}
f_t(360°) &= (1 - t)f_0(360°) + tf_1(360°)\\
&= (1 - t)f_0(0°) + (1 - t)n \cdot 360° + tf_1(0°) + tn \cdot 360°\\
&= (1 - t)f_0(0°) + tf_1(0°) + n \cdot 360°\\
&= f_0(0°) + n \cdot 360°,
\end{aligned}$$

so that $f_t(0°)$ and $f_t(360°)$ indeed represent the same point of $C$ at each instant $t$.

(We note that this transforming process means a flattening out of the folds, if $f_1$ should be the mapping defined by $f_1(a) = na$ .).

We have proved:

*Two mappings of C into itself are in the same class if, and only if, they have the same degree.*

In particular, a mapping of *C* into itself can be continuously transformed into a mapping which sends the whole of *C* on to a single point if, and only if, its degree is 0.

## A second definition of degree

Can similar remarks be made about the continuous mappings of a spherical surface *S* into itself? Yes indeed, but then we must first define the degree of mapping anew.

The definition of the degree of mappings of the circle *C* into itself was based on our unrolling the circle on to a straight line by means of the angular coordinate and representing the mapping graphically. This does not work in the case of a spherical surface.

We can, however, also define the degree of a mapping in yet another – equivalent – way for *C*, which can then be extended to the case of *S*.

Let *g* now be the mapping of *C* into itself defined by

$$g(a) = na \qquad (n \text{ integral}).$$

Points whose angular coordinates differ by $\frac{p}{|n|} \cdot 360°$ ($p = 0, 1, \ldots, |n| - 1$) have the same image; the image of *C* covers *C* just $|n|$ times; each point has exactly $|n|$ inverse images. This does not have to hold for an arbitrary mapping of degree *n*; as soon as a fold is inserted into the mapping, some points will be covered more often, in fact twice more, in general. This remark also shows, however, what has to be done: the inverse images of a point are to be counted

158

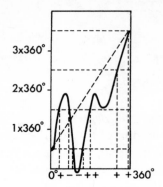

**Figure 5·15**

algebraically, positive if the point is covered in the positive direction of describing $C$, negative in the case of a negative direction of covering. For example, in the graphical representation (figure 5·15) I find the inverse images of 180° by drawing horizontal lines at $180° + m . 360°$ ($m$ integral) and seeking their point of intersection with the graphical representation of $f$. The corresponding $a$ are solutions of

$$f(a) = 180° + m . 360°;$$

there are eight in the figure; of these, the ones where the curve increases through the value $180° + m . 360°$ are to be counted positive, those where the curve decreases through the value $180° + m . 360°$ are to be counted negative and those where the curve touches only the horizontal lines at $180° + m . 360°$ are to be ignored. Calculating algebraically in this way, we get $5 - 2 + 0 = 3$ inverse images, i.e. as many as are given by the degree of the mapping.

If we work like this, each point has exactly $n$ (not $|n|$) inverse images under $g$ if

$$g(a) = na \qquad \text{($n$ integral)}.$$

If a mapping is changed continuously, inverse images of some points can appear or disappear, but only in pairs, of which one is counted positive, the other negative (a single one could possibly appear or disappear, but then it is one of the kind that is not counted). The number of inverse images remains constant under continuous changes of the mapping, and since all can be obtained from mappings $g$ with

$$g(a) = na \qquad (n \text{ integral})$$

we get:

*The degree of a mapping is equal to the number of inverse images of a point, counted algebraically.*

The foregoing is still not quite true. One can imagine mappings where infinitely many, ever narrower folds occur. A point can then have infinitely many inverse images. One then does not really know how to work with the infinite number of plus and minus signs. It is of help to replace the mapping $f$ first of all by a neighbouring $f'$, whose graphical representation is piecewise linear, and count the (then finite) number of inverse images under $f'$ of a point (algebraically, of course); it is of course necessary to convince oneself that it does not matter which neighbouring $f'$ replaces $f$. However, we had better not go into such fine points.

## Mappings of spheres

We are now prepared to deal with mappings $f$ of the spherical surface $S$ into itself. It is more convenient in this to imagine $S$ not as a curved surface, but as a polyhedron such as a tetrahedron; we will, as required, further subdivide the faces of this tetrahedron into smaller triangles.

We now provide $S$ with an orientation, i.e. standing on $S$, we say what anticlockwise means. The triangles $abc$ of any subdivision of $S$ are then provided with a rotational sense, which can be either $\overrightarrow{abca}$ or $\overrightarrow{cbac}$.

We first assume that the mapping $f$ maps triangles of one subdivision on to triangles of a (possibly different) subdivision, and in fact maps each single triangle barycentrically (see chapter 6), i.e. so that the centre of gravity of weights $m_a$, $m_b$, $m_c$ at $a$, $b$, $c$ corresponds to the centre of gravity of weights $m_a$, $m_b$, $m_c$ at $a'$, $b'$, $c'$. We now count the inverse images of each image triangle, and in fact algebraically; positive if $a'$ $b'$ $c'$ is oriented like $abc$, and negative if the mapping reverses the orientation. It can be seen that under $f$ each image triangle has the same number of inverse images (counted algebraically); if I leave an image triangle at a fold of the mapping, I can in fact lose or gain inverse images, but then always just as many positive as negative ones.

The algebraic number of inverse images of a triangle is again called the degree of the mapping $f$, for the moment defined for a mapping $f$ which maps triangles of a subdivision on to triangles of a subdivision. In order to define the degree of an arbitrary continuous mapping $f$, one must approximate $f$ by an $f$ of the above type and show that each approximation gives the same value for the degree of the mapping.

Finally, one can again show that two mappings of the same class (i.e. two mappings which are continuously transformable into each other) have the same degree, and, conversely, that two mappings of the same degree belong to the same class.

Let us now imagine $S$ as a spherical surface again! The 'identity' mapping, which maps each point on to itself, has degree 1; the mapping which associates with each point its antipode has degree $-1$, since it reverses the rotational sense of $S$. The mapping which maps the whole of $S$ on to a single point of $S$ is of degree 0. A mapping of degree $n > 0$ can be obtained as follows: imagine $S$ as the earth and map any point on to the point with $n$ times its longitude and unchanged latitude. The equator and each circle of latitude are then each mapped on to themselves, so that in fact their image covers them $n$ times. Under this mapping, each point (apart from the poles) has exactly $n$ inverse images, which are all to be counted positive. The image covers $S$ exactly $n$ times.

The degree of a mapping is preserved under continuous transformations. In particular, the identity mapping (of degree 1) cannot be continuously transformed into a mapping under which the image leaves a point of $S$ uncovered, since this has indeed degree 0. Formulated more concretely:

Let a wooden sphere be enclosed in a rubber cover (a spherical surface). It is impossible to so fold and deform this rubber cover (without tearing it) that a part of the wooden sphere becomes visible.

This seems obvious. How profound seemingly obvious things can be, if we want to prove them mathematically, becomes clear from the above ideas.

## A remarkable curve

One can also learn in topology that what we at first sight consider to be obvious, need not be true.

162

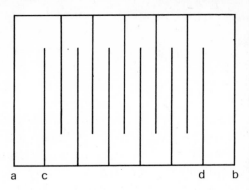

**Figure 5·16**

a     c                       d    b

Can one cut a hole in a piece of paper the size of one of the pages of this book through which a man can crawl?

Yes, this is extremely easy to do. Fold the paper symmetrically: figure 16 represents the folded paper, with *ab* as the fold. Make cuts in the folded paper as in figure 16 and finally cut through the fold as well, but only from *c* to *d*. Unfolding the paper, we find a hole of the required size.

Moreover, this can also be done with a piece of paper the size of a stamp, only one needs to make more cuts.

What strikes us here is that a surface can be cut up into something resembling a line. This can be better seen as follows:

A square (figure 5·17*a*) is divided into four squares 1, 2, 3, 4 whose sides are half the length of the original square's sides; 1 and 4 are separated by a cut along their common boundary. This was the first step. At the second (left half of figure 5·17*b*) the squares are further divided and numbered according to the figure; 1 and 4 are always separated along their common boundary. The third step is indicated in the right half of figure 5·17*b*; it is not in fact drawn in on the left, but must be carried out there, too. At the third step, too, the squares (of the second step) are divided into four and numbered (figure 5·17*c*), and the cut is always made between 1 and 4. We

**Figure 5·17**

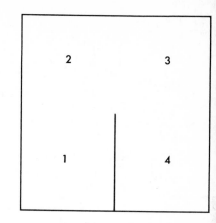

a

b

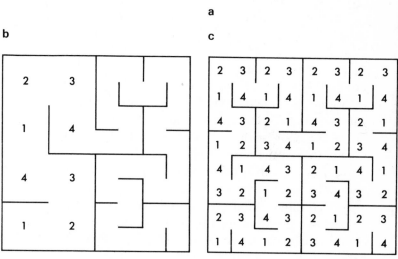

c

proceed similarly at the fourth step, and must imagine this process continued a fifth, sixth, seventh time, up to infinity – a sequence of even longer and narrower labyrinths should result. For this to succeed, we must so number the subsquares at each step that we can advance from the fourth subsquare of square number $a$ to the first one of square $a + 1$.

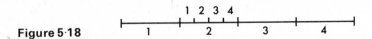

**Figure 5·18**

Thus we continue to infinity, and the surface of the square is then cut up into a curve. The square is mapped on to a curve. This is naturally not a continuous mapping. While cutting up the square we have duplicated or triplicated points. The result can be formulated more exactly as follows:

Take a line next to the square (figure 5·18) which, at the first step, is divided into sections 1, 2, 3, 4. At the second, the sections are again divided into 1, 2, 3, 4 and this continues to infinity. A point $x$ of the original line can be located as follows: at each stage note the number of the section on which it is lying. This becomes an infinite sequence, say 3241332144 ... Some points can be described in two such ways, e.g. the midpoints of the original line as 24444 ... and as 31111 ... We can determine the points of the square in a completely analogous way; at each stage we note down the number of the section where it is.

We now set up a correspondence between points of the line and square having the same sequence of numbers. This gives a continuous mapping of the line on to the square – the square is continuously traversed by the line's image. This continuous mapping is the inverse of the dissection we gave before. The line has been glued to a square.

This remarkable curve which covers a square was a discovery of the Italian mathematician G. Peano (1890).

# 6 Give me a place to stand and I will move the earth

Archimedes is reported to have astonished his fellow Syracusans and also, in the end, the Roman besiegers of his native town with all manner of technical wonders. These are supposed to have included an apparatus with which a single man could pull a heavily laden ship from the beach into the sea. 'Give me a place to stand on', this greatest mathematician of antiquity is supposed to have said to King Hieron, 'and I will move the earth.' According to another tradition this proud statement referred to the principle of the lever, to which Archimedes had devoted a treatise. The lever can of course be used to lift a heavy weight with little force.

The lever will be the starting point for the mathematics in this chapter.

### The lever

Two children sit on a see-saw (figure 6·1). The see-saw drops on the heavier one's side. It only stays in equilibrium, if they both are the same weight.

If, however, it is still to remain in equilibrium in spite of the difference in weight, what are the children to do? Well, the heavy one moves a little nearer to the middle of the see-saw. A weight clearly presses less strongly, the nearer it is to the centre of rotation; it is as if it has become lighter. Or the lighter child moves slightly farther out, the same weight clearly pressing more strongly there.

A swimmer runs along a diving board (figure 6·2). The farther he gets, the more the plank bends. The diver's weight presses more strongly, the farther he is from the board's support.

**Figure 6·1**

167

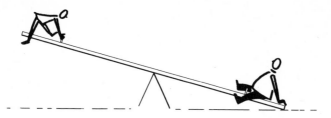

**Figure 6·2**

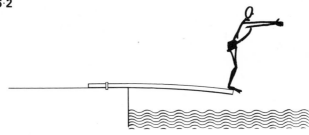

**Figure 6·3**

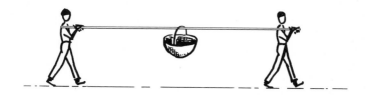

Two men carry a basket on a pole (figure 6·3). One follows the other; the pole rests horizontally on their shoulders. If the basket hangs in the middle, they both have to carry the same amount. If the basket is moved, part of the weight is shifted from the man who is farther from the basket to the one who is nearer to it. This is so because the force a man uses to support the pole has greater effect where the distance from the basket is larger.

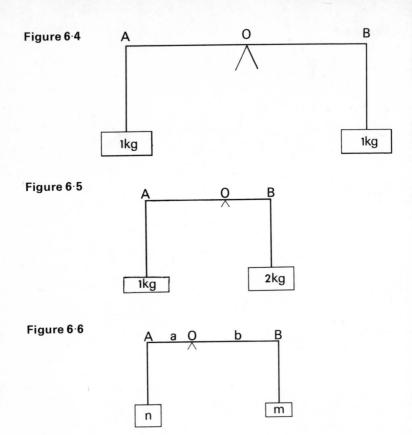

**Figure 6·4**

**Figure 6·5**

**Figure 6·6**

A balance is in equilibrium when the same weight presses on the right and left balance pans – at least when the balance involved is as in figure 6·4, with equal right and left arms. With unequal armlengths it is different. In figure 6·5 a balance is sketched whose left arm ($OA$) is twice as long as its right arm ($OB$) – the balance beam rotates about $O$, where it is supported.[1] If there is to be equilibrium here, the weight

1 In this work we always consider the balance arm as 'weightless', i.e. so that we can ignore its real weight.

attached at $B$ must be twice that at $A$. More generally, if the arm lengths satisfy

$$OA : OB = a : b$$

the weights attached at $A$ and $B$ must be in the ratio $b : a$, if equilibrium is required (figure 6·6).

We can express this differently. A weight of $m$ lb. exerts a force of $m$ lb. If it is attached at a distance $a$ from $O$, the product $ma$ of force (weight) and armlength is ascribed to it as moment; similarly, a force of $n$ lb, if acting on the arm at a distance $b$ from $O$, has moment $nb$.

Thus, if the weight is doubled and left at the same spot, the moment is doubled; if the weight is not altered and its distance from $O$ is doubled, the moment is also doubled. If the weight is doubled while the distance is simultaneously halved, the moment remains the same; similarly if the distance is doubled and the weight halved.

Equal weights $m$ on a balance with equal armlengths $a$ produce the moment $ma$ on the right and left. The moments are equal, and there is equilibrium. If the left arm of the balance has length $a$, the right arm length $b$, and weights $m$ and $n$ are attached at $A$ and $B$ respectively, we get on the left the moment $ma$ as the product of weight $m$ and armlength $a$, on the right the moment $nb$. For there to be equilibrium, both moments must be equal,

$$ma = nb.$$

In fact this is the same as

$$m : n = b : a,$$

**Figure 6·7**

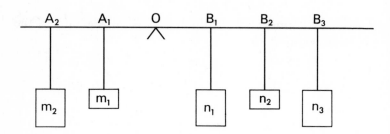

or, the weights must be inversely proportional to the armlengths.

We now imagine a beam supported at $O$ and on which weights are movable (figure 6·7). The weights $m_1, m_2, \ldots$ are attached at $A_1, A_2, \ldots$ at distances $a_1, a_2, \ldots$ from $O$ respectively. Similarly, the weights $n_1, n_2, \ldots$ are supported at $B_1, B_2, \ldots$ at distances $b_1, b_2, \ldots$ from $O$ respectively.

Form the moments and add them. On the left we have the total moment

$$m_1a_1 + m_2a_2 + \ldots$$

and on the right

$$n_1b_1 + n_2b_2 + \ldots.$$

There is equilibrium, if

$$m_1a_1 + m_2a_2 + \ldots = n_1b_1 + n_2b_2 + \ldots.$$

If I hang two weights $m$ and $m'$ at a point $A$, say, at a distance $a$ from $O$, they give the total moment

$$ma + m'a.$$

But instead of this, I can at once hang the weight $m + m'$ there, with the moment

$$(m + m')a.$$

They must both come to the same thing, and indeed we know from algebra that

$$(m + m')a = ma + m'a.$$

All this can be constructed still more elegantly, if moments are more cunningly interpreted. A weight on the right of $O$ wants to rotate the balance beam clockwise (as seen by the observer); one on the left of $O$ acts on the balance beam in the direction of an anticlockwise rotation. We now furnish moments with a sign: 'plus' when they are clockwise and 'minus' when they are anticlockwise. This can also be obtained as follows: distances on the balance beam (measured from $O$) are counted positive to the right, negative to the left, and these distances are then multiplied by the weights to give the moments. If one factor in a product is given the opposite sign, the whole product gets the opposite sign. Thus, according to the new rules, all moments derived from weights on the left must be prefixed by a negative sign.

When, according to the old rules, we said that total left and right moments have to be equal, we now say more simply:

*The total moment must be zero.*

That is, we add up *all* moments, all left moments automatically having the negative sign.

We now put the question in a slightly different way. A

balance beam with weights attached is again given. Now, however, the question is, where must I support it so that it is in equilibrium?

I first of all choose the origin arbitrarily. Weights $m_1$, $m_2$, ... are then at distances $a_1$, $a_2$, ... calculated from this origin (these distances are again to be taken positive on the right of $O$, negative on the left of $O$). With respect to this origin, the total is

$$M = m_1 a_1 + m_2 a_2 + \ldots$$

If I move the origin to $x$, the new distances become $a_1 - x$, $a_2 - x$, ... and the moment becomes

$$m_1(a_1 - x) + m_2(a_2 - x) + \ldots = (m_1 a_1 + m_2 a_2 + \ldots) - $$
$$- (m_1 + m_2 + \ldots)x$$
$$= M - mx,$$

where $m = m_1 + m_2 + \ldots$ is the total weight. Should $x$ as point of support guarantee equilibrium, the new moment must be zero, i.e. $M = mx$ or $x = \dfrac{M}{m}$.

The point where a balance beam with weights attached has to be supported to obtain equilibrium is called its *centre of gravity*. We have shown that

*The position of the centre of gravity is obtained by dividing the total moment by the total weight.*

The origin, from which distances are measured, may be arbitrarily chosen for this purpose. Indeed, if it is moved to $c$, the distances $a_1$, $a_2$, ... become $a_1 - c$, $a_2 - c$, ...; the moment changes to $M - mc$, and $\dfrac{M}{m}$, from which the centre of gravity is to be calculated, is diminished by $c$ exactly, as we expected.

I now pick out some of the weights on the beam, say $m_1$, $m_2$, ... hanging at $a_1$, $a_2$, ... apart from these, however, there can be still more weights $n_1$, $n_2$, ... at $b_1$, $b_2$, ... which for the moment don't interest me. I now replace the selected weights by their total weight which I put at their centre of gravity. I note that the centre of gravity of the whole system is unaltered by this.

Indeed, the contribution of the picked weights to the total moment is $m_1a_1 + m_2a_2 + \ldots$; the contribution of the new weight $m_1+m_2+ \ldots$ to the total moment is $(m_1+m_2+\ldots)x$, if $x$ is the centre of gravity of the picked weights. But we had

$$x = \frac{m_1a_1 + m_2a_2 + \ldots}{m_1 + m_2 + \ldots},$$

and this means that the contribution of the new weight to the total moment is exactly the same as that of the picked weights. Consequently, the centre of gravity of the whole system remains unchanged.

The result can also be formulated as follows:

*A system of weights may be replaced by its total weight placed at the centre of gravity.*

We look one step further: we want to allow negative weights, too. Let us first of all think of the balance in figure 6·7. What should we understand by a negative weight there? Clearly, one which pulls upwards. This can be realised by reversing a weight's direction of force by means of a pulley:

**Figure 6·8**

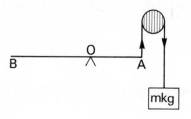

see figure 6·8, where at the point $A$ a force of $m$ lb pulls upwards. Such a negative weight of $m$ lb at $A$ has clearly the same effect as a positive one of $m$ lb at $B$, if $B$ lies as far to the left of $O$ as $A$ does to the right. If I work out the moments as before, the weight $-m$ at $a$ contributes

$$(-m)a,$$

the weight $m$ at $-a$ contributes:

$$m(-a).$$

By the rules of algebra, both are equal to
$$-ma.$$

It is further interesting to note that a negative weight at $B$ has the same effect as the corresponding positive one at $A$. In the first case, we get as contribution to the moment

$$(-m)(-a),$$

in the second:
$$ma,$$
which, by well-known rules, is in fact the same thing.

We can now imagine all kinds of positive and negative weights on a balance beam and calculate their total moment. The position of the centre of gravity is again obtained from the total weight $m$ and the total moment $M$ as

$$\frac{M}{m}.$$

But now we have to be careful. Since positive and negative weights occur, the total weight can be 0. One cannot divide by 0, however. Thus, there need not always be a centre of gravity. This is, of course, quite clear. For example, if I attach a weight of 1 lb at each of two different points on a balance beam, one weight being normal, the other over a pulley, i.e. pulling upwards, the balance beam can never be in equilibrium, wherever I support it.

## The plane

We now consider the plane, i.e. a weightless, horizontal lamina on which weights are placed. We seek the point, called the *centre of gravity*, where the lamina has to be supported if it is to be in equilibrium.

Let three weights of 1 lb, say, be placed at the vertices of a triangle ABC (figure 6·9). By what we have learnt earlier, we can replace the weights of 1 lb at $A$ and $B$ by one of 2 lb at the midpoint $F$ of $AB$. We then have a weight of 1 lb at $C$ and one of 2 lb at $F$. They again have a centre of gravity $S$, which lies between $C$ and $F$. $S$ lies so that the total moment of these two weights becomes zero, i.e. $S$ divides the straight line $CF$ inversely to the ratio to the weights:

$$CS : SF = 2 : 1.$$

$S$ is thus precisely the point which in geometry is usually called the centroid of the triangle $ABC$.

If we had first replaced the weights at $A$ and $C$ by a double one at the midpoint $E$ of $AC$, we would have arrived at the

176

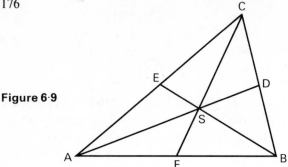

**Figure 6·9**

same point $S$. As is well known, the lines joining the vertices to the midpoints of the opposite sides intersect in the centroid $S$, which itself divides the joining lines in the ratio 2 : 1 (from the vertex).

After this special case, we go on to determine the centre of gravity of weights on a lamina in general. We do as above: two weights are replaced by their sum, which we put at their centre of gravity. We continue in this way, until finally all weights are combined in one point. This is the centre of gravity.

This now raises the question: is this point uniquely determined? If the weights are combined in another order, something else could conceivably result.

In fact, the centre of gravity is uniquely fixed (at least, if the sum of the weights is not zero). In order to show this, we again introduce moments. Just as before the moment with respect to a point was defined, we now define it with respect to a straight line, also called the axis.

We draw a straight line $X$ in the plane and on it distinguish a left and a right side in any way we please; we reckon distances from this straight line or axis negatively on the left and positively on the right. Positive weights on different

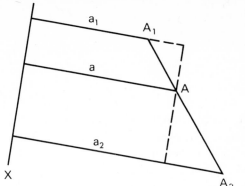

**Figure 6·10**

sides of the axis want to turn the plane in opposite directions.
A weight $m$ at a distance $a$ (positive or negative) from the
axis $X$ produces the moment $ma$ with respect to the axis $X$.
We can form the total moment with respect to the axis $X$
of these moments.

What happens to the total moment when two weights $m_1$,
$m_2$ at the points $A_1$, $A_2$ are replaced by the weight $m_1 + m_2$
at their centre of gravity $A$? (figure 6·10). $A$ divides the line
$A_1A_2$ in the ratio $m_2 : m_1$. $A_1$, $A_2$, $A$ are at distances $a_1$, $a_2$, $a$
respectively from $X$. Drawing the lines parallel to $X$ through
$A$, we see that $a-a_1 : a_2-a = m_2 : m_1$ also. Thus

$$m_1(a-a_1) = m_2(a_2-a),$$
$$(m_1 + m_2)a = m_1a_1 + m_2a_2.$$

Here, the total moment of the weights at $A_1$ and $A_2$ is on the
right, and the moment of the combined weight at the centre
of gravity $A$ is on the left. It is thus seen that:

The total moment with respect to the axis $X$ is unchanged,
if two weights are replaced by their combined weight at the
pair's centre of gravity.

The question whether the centre of gravity of the weights
is fixed irrespective of the manner of construction can now

178

be partly answered: in any case, the moment of the centre of gravity with respect to the axis $X$ is uniquely fixed; indeed, it is equal to the total moment of the given weights. This, however, also determines the distance of the centre of gravity from $X$, since I obtain it by dividing the moment by the total mass (which should not be zero).

I can now choose the axis $X$ quite arbitrarily, and this shows that the distance of the centre of gravity from each straight line in the plane is completely determined. The centre of gravity itself is also fixed by this, however.

Actually, it is sufficient to have two intersecting straight lines $X$ and $Y$ in order to fix a point by means of its distances from them (figure 6·11); indeed, it is only necessary to draw lines parallel to $X$ and $Y$ at the corresponding given distances (positive or negative) and to ascertain their point of intersection.

One further remark: if the total weight is zero, we cannot expect a centre of gravity. It could, however, also happen with a non-zero total weight that during the *construction* of

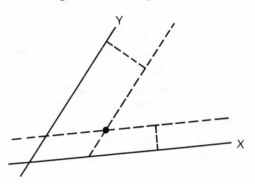

**Figure 6·11**

the centre of gravity vanishing weights occur. If $m_1$ and $m_2$, say, are equal and of opposite sign, we may not start our construction by combining $m_1$ and $m_2$.

Now on the other hand

$$m_1 + m_2 + m_3 + \ldots \neq 0,$$

and hence it is impossible that *every* pair of weights is equal and of opposite sign. One can thus certainly find two whose sum is not zero, and this holds at each of the following steps.

## Barycentric coordinates

Let $A$, $B$ be two distinct points of the plane. If weights $m$, $n$ with non-vanishing sum are placed at $A$, $B$ respectively, the centre of gravity $Q$ lies on the straight line $AB$, in fact so that

$$m \cdot \overrightarrow{QA} + n \cdot \overrightarrow{QB} = 0,$$

i.e.

$$\overrightarrow{AQ} : \overrightarrow{QB} = n : m.$$

If, on the other hand, we wish the centre of gravity to be at $Q$, we have only to choose $m$, $n$ so that their ratio is $\overrightarrow{AQ} : \overrightarrow{QB}$. In particular, the centre of gravity is at $A$ if $n = 0$ and at $B$ if $m = 0$.

In all these cases, the only important thing is the ratio of $m$ and $n$; multiplication of $m$, $n$ by the same number does not alter the centre of gravity.

The points *between* $A$ and $B$ are obtained as centres of gravity, if positive weights are taken. If the weights have different signs, the centre of gravity lies outside the segment $AB$, in fact on the side of the weight with the greater absolute value.

At all events, the points of the straight line $AB$ can be described by means of the ratio of the weights $m : n$.

We now take three, non-collinear points $A_1$, $A_2$, $A_3$ in the plane. Corresponding to weights $m_1$, $m_2$, $m_3$ at these points with non-vanishing sum there is a centre of gravity $P$. Again, only the ratio of $m_1$, $m_2$, $m_3$ is important. Conversely, each prescribed point $P$ of the plane can be obtained as the centre of gravity of suitable weights at $A_1$, $A_2$, $A_3$. This is done as follows: if the prescribed $P$ coincides with $A_1$, put $m_1 = 1$, $m_2 = m_3 = 0$; the centre of gravity of these weights is indeed $A_1$. We proceed similarly if $P = A_2$ or $A_3$. Now let $P$ be distinct from $A_1$, $A_2$, $A_3$. The join of $P$ to one of the vertices could be parallel to the opposite side; but if that does happen, it cannot hold for all three vertices at the same time. Thus, at least one of the straight lines $PA_i$ intersects the opposite side $A_jA_k(j \neq i, k \neq i)$. Let us suppose that $PA_1$ intersects the side $A_2A_3$ in $Q$ (in the other cases we would proceed similarly): see figure 6·12. At $A_2$, $A_3$ place weights $m_2$, $m_3$ whose centre of gravity is $Q$; this is done in the manner shown above. We now imagine the weight $m_2 + m_3$ at $Q$, which represents the weights $m_2$, $m_3$ at $A_2$, $A_3$ taken together. Then place the weight $m_1$ at $A_1$ which is so chosen that the centre of gravity of $m_1$ at $A_1$ and $m_2 + m_3$ at $Q$ is exactly $P$; we saw before that this works. Then $P$ is indeed the centre of gravity of the weights $m_1$, $m_2$, $m_3$ at $A_1$, $A_2$, $A_3$ as was required.

All points $P$ of the plane can thus be described by means of

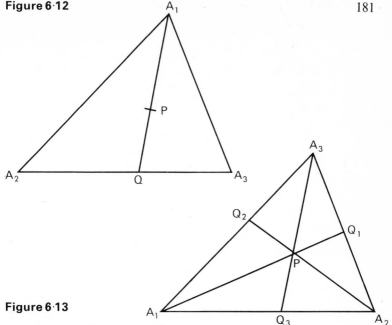

**Figure 6·12**                                                      181

**Figure 6·13**

weights $m_1$, $m_2$, $m_3$; placed at $A_1$, $A_2$, $A_3$ they give $P$ as centre of gravity. In this, only the ratio of $m_1$, $m_2$, $m_3$ is important; if we divide at once by the total weight (this is of course not zero) we can get it to be 1. In the following we therefore assume that $m_1 + m_2 + m_3 = 1$.

The three numbers $m_1$, $m_2$, $m_3$ which belong to a point $P$ are called its *barycentric coordinates*. (Centre of gravity coordinates.) Barycentric coordinates were introduced in 1827 by Möbius.

We consider a point $P$ with barycentric coordinates $m_1$, $m_2$, $m_3$ and join it to $A_1$, $A_2$, $A_3$, the opposite sides being intersected in $Q_1$, $Q_2$, $Q_3$ as in figure 6·13. Thus

$$\frac{\overrightarrow{A_1Q_3}}{\overrightarrow{Q_3A_2}} = \frac{m_2}{m_3}, \quad \frac{\overrightarrow{A_2Q_1}}{\overrightarrow{Q_1A_3}} = \frac{m_3}{m_1}, \quad \frac{\overrightarrow{A_3Q_2}}{\overrightarrow{Q_2A_1}} = \frac{m_1}{m_2}.$$

**Figure 6·14**

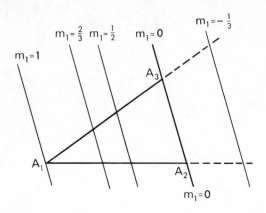

Multiplying this we get

$$\vec{A_1 Q_3} \cdot \vec{A_2 Q_1} \cdot \vec{A_3 Q_2} = \vec{Q_1 A_3} \cdot \vec{Q_2 A_1} \cdot \vec{Q_3 A_2},$$

a theorem which is named after the mathematician Menelaus.

For $m_1 = 1$, $m_2 = m_3 = 0$ we get $A_1$, for $m_2 = 1$, $m_1 = m_3 = 0$ we get $A_2$, for $m_3 = 1$, $m_1 = m_2 = 0$ we get $A_3$. All points with $m_1 = 0$ lie on the straight line $A_2 A_3$, all with $m_2 = 0$ on the straight line $A_1 A_3$, all with $m_3 = 0$ on the straight line $A_1 A_2$.

$m_1$ is positive on the side of $A_2 A_3$ where $A_1$ lies, and negative on the other. The corresponding result holds for $m_2$ and $m_3$. The points for which all weights are positive are precisely those inside the triangle $A_1 A_2 A_3$.

We have seen: for $P = A_1$ we have $m_1 = 1$, and the points $P$ with $m_1 = 0$ lie on $A_2 A_3$. Where now do those with $m_1 = \frac{1}{2}$ lie? Should $m_1 = \frac{1}{2}$, we must also have $m_2 + m_3 = \frac{1}{2}$; we thus have to place equal weights at $A_1$ and at an arbitrary point $Q$ of the straight line $A_2 A_3$; the centre of gravity $P$ then runs parallel to $A_2 A_3$ and bisects the line from $A_1$ to $A_2 A_3$. See figure 6·14, where we have drawn in several 'level curves' $m_1$. One can verify that they must be parallel

**Figure 6·15** 183

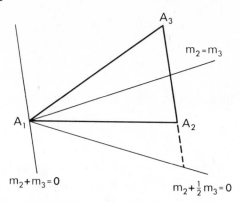

straight lines; we shall, however, soon prove this generally as well.

We put a further question: for which points $P$ is $m_2 = m_3$? We must thus put equal weights at $A_2$ and $A_3$; their centre of gravity lies in the middle. After that, we can put another weight at $A_1$, the centre of gravity of the three weights lies on the joining straight line. See figure 6·15 where we have drawn in more lines of the same kind.

More generally, we write down the equation:

(*) $$p_1 m_1 + p_2 m_2 + p_3 m_3 = p_0$$

where $p_0$, $p_1$, $p_2$, $p_3$ are given numbers, and ask which points $P$ satisfy it, i.e. which points $P$ have coordinates $m_1$, $m_2$, $m_3$ which, on substitution, satisfy the equation.

We note that in any case the equation

(**) $$m_1 + m_2 + m_3 = 1$$

must be satisfied. Thus, instead of equation (*) we can just as well solve the equation

$$(p_1 - p_0)m_1 + (p_2 - p_0)m_2 + (p_3 - p_0)m_3 = 0,$$

which results if we subtract (**) multiplied by $p_0$ from (*).

We can hence restrict ourselves at once to equations

$$(***) \qquad q_1 m_1 + q_2 m_2 + q_3 m_3 = 0.$$

with given $q_1$, $q_2$, $q_3$.

Equations (**) and (***) have in general common solutions. There are none only if they contradict each other, namely if $q_1 = q_2 = q_3 \neq 0$; then, on the one hand, the sum of the weights must equal 1, while, on the other, it must equal 0. If $q_1 = q_2 = q_3 = 0$, every point $P$ satisfies the conditions.

I note: if $P$ and $P'$ satisfy equations (**) and (***), so too does every point $R$ on the straight line $PP'$. Indeed, each such point $R$ can be described as the centre of gravity of weights $a$, $\beta$ at $P$, $P'$ respectively. Now let $P$ be the centre of gravity of the weights $m_1$, $m_2$, $m_3$ at $A_1$, $A_2$, $A_3$ and $P'$ be the centre of gravity of the weights $m_1'$, $m_2'$, $m_3'$ at $A_1$, $A_2$, $A_3$. Then I can regard $R$ as the centre of gravity of the weights $a m_1 + \beta m_1'$, $a m_2 + \beta m_2'$, $a m_3 + \beta m_3'$ at $A_1$, $A_2$, $A_3$. On the other hand

$$q_1 (a m_1 + \beta m_1') + q_2 (a m_2 + \beta m_2') + q_3 (a m_3 + \beta m_3') =$$
$$= a(q_1 m_1 + q_2 m_2 + q_3 m_3) + \beta(q_1 m_1' + q_2 m_2' + q_3 m_3') =$$
$$= 0,$$

since the coordinates of $P$ and $P'$ respectively satisfy equation (***). We have shown that $R$ satisfies it too, and this is what we wanted to prove. (We can afterwards still divide by the sum of the weights, so that (**) is satisfied as well.)

Thus together with two points $P$ and $P'$, all points of the straight line $PP'$ satisfy equation (***). If the solution

**Figure 6·16**

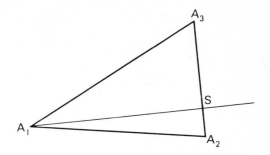

consists of more than one straight line, it is the whole plane, and this is precisely the case when it happens that $q_1 = q_2 = q_3 = 0$. If $q_1 = q_2 = q_3 \neq 0$, there is no solution at all, and in all other cases the solution is a straight line.

Can we get every straight line in this way? The answer is yes. We first take a straight line passing through $A_1$ (see figure 6·16). The point with barycentric coordinates $m_1 = 1$, $m_2 = m_3 = 0$ must lie on it and thus satisfy equation (***), i.e. $q_1 = 0$. The equation for the given straight line must thus in any case be of the form

$$q_2 m_2 + q_3 m_3 = 0.$$

The point of intersection $S$ of the given straight line and $A_2 A_3$ satisfies

$$\overrightarrow{SA_2} . m_2 + \overrightarrow{SA_3} . m_3 = 0$$

Hence, if $q_2$, $q_3$ are taken proportional to $\overrightarrow{SA_2}$, $\overrightarrow{SA_3}$, $A_1$ and $S$ satisfy the equation

$$q_2 m_2 + q_3 m_3 = 0.$$

We have thereby found the equation for the given straight line. If by chance the given straight line is parallel to $A_2 A_3$, we have to take $q_2 = -q_3 = 1$, say.

186

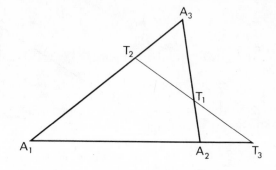

**Figure 6·17**

If the given straight line passes through another vertex of the triangle $A_1A_2A_3$, we proceed similarly. If it does not pass through any of the vertices, it intersects at least two of the sides, for example the side $A_2A_3$ in $T_1$ and the side $A_1A_2$ in $T_3$ (see figure 6·17).

The barycentric coordinates of $T_1$ satisfy

$$m_1 = 0. \; m_2 . \overrightarrow{T_1A_2} + m_3 . \overrightarrow{T_1A_3} = 0.$$

Those of $T_2$ satisfy

$$m_2 = 0, \; m_3 . \overrightarrow{T_2A_3} + m_1 . \overrightarrow{T_2A_1} = 0.$$

For $T_1$ to lie on the given straight line with equation

$$q_1m_1 + q_2m_2 + q_3m_3 = 0,$$

we must have

$$q_2 : q_3 = \overrightarrow{T_1A_2} : \overrightarrow{T_1A_3}.$$

For $T_2$ to lie on this straight line, we must have

$$q_3 : q_1 = \overrightarrow{T_2A_3} : \overrightarrow{T_2A_1}.$$

One must thus specify $q_1$, $q_2$, $q_3$ and in so doing obtain an equation for the given straight line.

One more deduction from figure 6·17: we also have

$$q_1 : q_2 = \overrightarrow{T_3A_1} : \overrightarrow{T_3A_2}.$$

If the last three equations are multiplied together, the value 1 results on the left. Thus

$$\overrightarrow{T_1A_2} . \overrightarrow{T_2A_3} . \overrightarrow{T_3A_1} = \overrightarrow{T_1A_3} . \overrightarrow{T_2A_1} . \overrightarrow{T_3A_2}.$$

This equation is named after Ceva, an Italian mathematician of the seventeenth century. It looks very similar to the one of Menelaus.

One more remark which we use later on

$$p_1m_1 + p_2m_2 + p_3m_3 = p_0$$

also represents a straight line, since it can be reduced to (\*\*). If I change $p_0$ into $p_0'$, I obtain

$$p_1m_1 + p_2m_2 + p_3m_3 = p_0'.$$

If $p_0 \neq p_0'$, these two conditions stand in contradiction to each other. Thus, there cannot be a system $m_1$, $m_2$, $m_3$ which satisfies both, and hence also no point which lies on both the straight lines.

The two equations thus lead to parallel straight lines. For various $p_0$, (\*) represents parallel straight lines.

## Linear programming

Chocolate consists of cocoa, sugar and milk. Depending on the mixture, we get different types of chocolate. The mixing ratio distinguishes the type of chocolate.

188

Let the mixing ratio be $m_1 : m_2 : m_3$ (cocoa to sugar to milk). We draw a triangle $A_1A_2A_3$ in the plane. Let the cocoa correspond to $A_1$, the sugar to $A_2$, the milk to $A_3$. We let the centre of gravity of the weights $m_1$, $m_2$, $m_3$ at $A_1$, $A_2$, $A_3$ respectively correspond to the chocolate with mixing ratio $m_1 : m_2 : m_3$.

Each type of chocolate is then characterised by a point of the triangle $A_1A_2A_3$. Points outside the triangle are not considered, since outside at least one of the weights $m_1$, $m_2$, $m_3$ is negative.

Pure cocoa is represented by the point $A_1$, pure sugar by $A_2$, pure milk by $A_3$. Bitter chocolates lie near to $A_1$, sweet ones near to $A_2$, milk chocolates near to $A_3$.

I should like to make a chocolate to my own taste. I can get hold of three kinds to which the points $B_1$, $B_2$, $B_3$ in the triangle correspond. Let the chocolate of my choice correspond to the point $C$. Can I make it by mixing the types $B_1$, $B_2$, $B_3$, and in what ratio must I mix them?

Let us call this mixing ratio $n_1$, $n_2$, $n_3$. I get the mixture by placing weights $n_1$, $n_2$, $n_3$ at $B_1$, $B_2$, $B_3$ respectively. The centre of gravity must then be exactly $C$ (see figure 6·18).

Thus, we have to specify the weights $n_1$, $n_2$, $n_3$ at $B_1$, $B_2$, $B_3$ so that their centre of gravity is the given $C$. Of course, $n_1$, $n_2$, $n_3$ cannot be negative. This means, however, that $C$ lies in the triangle $B_1B_2B_3$.

I can only make such chocolates as lie in the triangle $B_1B_2B_3$.

What does chocolate cost? That depends on the price of the components. Let the price per lb for cocoa be $p_1$, for

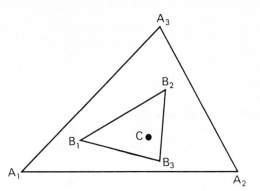

Figure 6·18

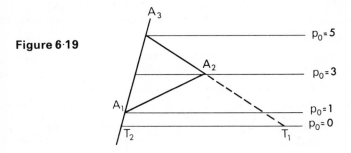

Figure 6·19

sugar $p_2$, for milk $p_3$. (The manufacturing costs are independent of the composition; we do not consider them.)

The price per lb of the chocolate with composition $m_1 : m_2 : m_3$ turns out to be

$$p_1m_1 + p_2m_2 + p_3m_3,$$

For chocolate in the same price range $p_0$, we have

$$p_1m_1 + p_2m_2 + p_3m_3 = p_0.$$

By what we saw in the previous section, chocolates in the same price range are collinear. We also saw that the straight lines belonging to different price ranges must be parallel. Let us suppose (and this may be quite wrong) that the prices of cocoa, sugar and milk are in the ratio 1 : 3 : 5.

In figure 6·19 we have indicated such price ranges. We have firstly calculated the straight line for the price range $p_0 = 0$. It must intersect $A_2A_3$ in $T_1$ so that $T_1A_2 : T_1A_3 = 3 : 5$. Further, it must intersect the straight line $A_3A_1$ in $T_2$ so that $T_2A_3 : T_2A_1 = 5 : 1$. It is determined by this. Naturally, no real chocolates correspond to the points of this straight line; they all lie outside the triangle $A_1A_2A_3$, of course. But in any case, the straight lines which correspond to other price ranges must be parallel to this one, in fact those of the price ranges 1, 3, 5 pass through $A_1$, $A_2$, $A_3$ respectively. The cheapest chocolate consists of pure cocoa, the most expensive of pure milk. Completing the system of parallel straight lines, we can read off the price range of each type of chocolate.

Let us now leave chocolate and turn to another problem!

A factory processes a raw material, in fact a fixed amount each day, which we take as our unit. It processes it in three different ways and thus produces three different end products I, II, III, with which it earns various amounts. The net profit is $p_1$, $p_2$, $p_3$ per unit of processed raw material respectively; it would thus be exactly $p_1$, $p_2$, $p_3$ if only the first, the second or the third article respectively were produced.

On a day when the three products are produced containing raw materials in the ratio $m_1 : m_2 : m_3$, the net profit is thus

$$P = p_1m_1 + p_2m_2 + p_3m_3.$$

We again represent the production ratio $m_1 : m_2 : m_3$ by the centre of gravity of weights $m_1$, $m_2$, $m_3$ at the vertices of the triangle $A_1A_2A_3$. The different levels of equal profit are parallel straight lines. If we assume that $p_1 : p_2 : p_3 = 1 : 3 : 5$, we can again use figure 6·19 for illustration.

One would preferably only produce the third product which gives the greatest profit. Unfortunately, this may not work. Suppose that, before it is an end product, the material must pass through four machines, in fact for different lengths of time, depending on what is to be produced.

We get a numerical table

|       | I     | II    | III    |
|-------|-------|-------|--------|
| $T$   | $t_1$ | $t_2$ | $t_3$  |
| $U$   | $u_1$ | $u_2$ | $u_3$  |
| $V$   | $v_1$ | $v_2$ | $v_3$  |
| $W$   | $w_1$ | $w_2$ | $w_3$, |

which expresses the following: unit raw material, if $I$ is produced, occupies machine $T$ for the period of time $t_1$, machine $U$ for the period of time $u_1$, etc. Similarly, if $II$ is to be made, machine $T$ is occupied for the period of time $t_2$, etc. (We again take the day as time unit.) Of course, each of the machines, $T$, $U$, $V$, $W$ has per day no more than one day of machine-time available.

If, on a given day, the ratio of the end products is fixed as $m_1 : m_2 : m_3$, machine $T$ is in use for a total period

$$t_1 m_1 + t_2 m_2 + t_3 m_3.$$

We must thus have

$$t_1 m_1 + t_2 m_2 + t_3 m_3 \leqslant 1.$$

Similarly, for the other machines:

$$u_1m_1 + u_2m_2 + u_3m_3 \leqslant 1,$$
$$v_1m_1 + v_2m_2 + v_3m_3 \leqslant 1,$$
$$w_1m_1 + w_2m_2 + w_3m_3 \leqslant 1.$$

We thus cannot dispose of the production ratio $m_1 : m_2 : m_3$ arbitrarily; we must take into account the above inequalities which stem from the capacity of the machines $T$, $U$, $V$, $W$.

Where do we now find the points in the figure which satisfy these inequalities? An equation

$$t_1m_1 + t_2m_2 + t_3m_3 = 1$$

is represented by a straight line; the points for which

$$t_1m_1 + t_2m_2 + t_3m_3 < 1 \text{ or } > 1$$

thus lie on one or the other side of the straight line. A half-plane bounded by a straight line corresponds to the inequality

$$t_1m_1 + t_2m_2 + t_3m_3 \leqslant 1.$$

We have here to satisfy four inequalities and correspondingly to give four half-planes. This is done in figure 6·20. The straight lines denoted by $T$, $U$, $V$, $W$ correspond to machines $T$, $U$, $V$, $W$; the side of these straight lines on which the half-plane in question lies is given by a small hatching. The part of the triangle belonging to all four half-planes is completely hatched. Points corresponding to allowed ratios $m_1 : m_2 : m_3$ thus lie here. These are production ratios which can be realised with regard to the capacity of the machines. A machine, say $T$, is used at full capacity, if the point re-

**Figure 6·20**

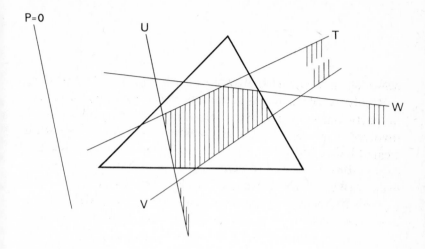

presenting the production ratio lies on the corresponding straight line, i.e. on $T$. We see that under the given conditions at most two machines can be used simultaneously at full capacity.

The straight lines could furthermore have been so situated that the inequalities have no common solution at all. For example, this is the case when $t_1$, $t_2$, $t_3$ are all $> 1$, since then $t_1m_1 + t_2m_2 + t_3m_3 > m_1 + m_2 + m_3 = 1$, i.e. $> 1$, while it should be $\leqslant 1$.

Another straight line $P = 0$ can be seen in figure 6·20. Here again, $P = p_1m_1 + p_2m_2 + p_3m_3$ is the net profit. We wish to make this as large as possible. This means that the straight line has to be moved parallel to itself until it meets the hatched area for the last time. Let the equation of the moved straight line be $P = k$. A point on $P = k$ gives a most profitable production ratio $m_1 : m_2 : m_3$; there may be only *one* such point, but there can also be several.

Problems like the one just tackled occur frequently

nowadays in the work of applied mathematicians. The posing and solving of such questions is called *programming*, and in particular, when linear equations and inequalities are involved, as here, 'linear programming'. The question treated here with three unknowns $m_1$, $m_2$, $m_3$ was particularly easy. In practice, problems with hundreds of unknowns occur which are solved with electronic computers. The treatment of a large problem can cost thousands, but the increased profit, obtained from knowing the best solution, can involve hundreds of thousands or millions.

A few more examples of such problems as occur in practice (but without solutions).

First, the *transport problem*: a company has ten factories in the world, $A_1$, ..., $A_{10}$, where it manufactures a particular product, in fact in the quantities $m_1$, ..., $m_{10}$. It has fifty distributing agencies $B_1$, ..., $B_{50}$ which take the quantities $n_1$, ..., $n_{50}$ of this product respectively. Of course, we must have $m_1 + ... + m_{10} = n_1 + ... + n_{50}$. The transport costs are known: for unit product, which is transported from $A_i$ to $B_j$, they amount to $u_{ij}$. The quantity $x_{ij}$ is transported from $A_i$ to $B_j$. How must one dispose of the unknown $x_{ij}$ so that the total transport costs will be as small as possible?

In order that the quantity $m_i$ is collected from $A_i$, we must have

$$x_{i1} + ... + x_{i\,50} = m_i \qquad \text{for } i = 1, ..., 10.$$

In order that the quantity $n_j$ arrives at $B_j$, we must have

$$x_{1j} + ... + x_{10\,j} = n_j \qquad \text{for } j = 1, ..., 50.$$

These are $10 + 50$ equations for the 500 unknowns $x_{ij}$. The total transport costs are

$$x_{11}u_{11} + \ldots + x_{10\,1}u_{10\,1} + \ldots + x_{10\,50}u_{10\,50}.$$

This has to be minimised.

Then the *warehouse problem*: a warehouse has a certain storage capacity for a fixed article. The price of the article is subject to known seasonal fluctuations. The market fluctuates likewise in a known manner with the time of year. One has to find the most advantageous buying scheme.

The *restaurant problem*: the table linen of a restaurant is sent to the laundry. Normal service takes one week, express service, which is more expensive, takes two days. If the linen is washed normally one has to buy more linen than if it is washed express. How much linen must one buy, and what proportion is to be washed normally, what proportion express, to make the most profit?

The *commercial traveller problem*: the commercial traveller has to visit fifty towns throughout the country in a fixed time. Which is the most convenient route? (No satisfactory method of solution for this problem has yet been found.)

An *amusing problem*: is monogamy the most satisfactory system of marriage? The population consists of men $A_i$ and women $B_j$. The esteem of $A_i$ and $B_j$ for each other is measured by the number $u_{ij}$. If $A_i$ spends the time $t_{ij}$ with $B_j$, the total esteem becomes the sum of the $t_{ij}u_{ij}$. This has of course to be maximised. It can be shown that the maximum in any case is reached when each man lives with only one woman and each woman lives with only one man.

Monogamy is thus a most suitable system of marriage.

To be sure, monogamy is also a most unsatisfactory system of marriage – the total esteem is also minimised by a monogamous matching of partners, but the pairs have then to be differently combined.

# 7 The world in
# a mirror

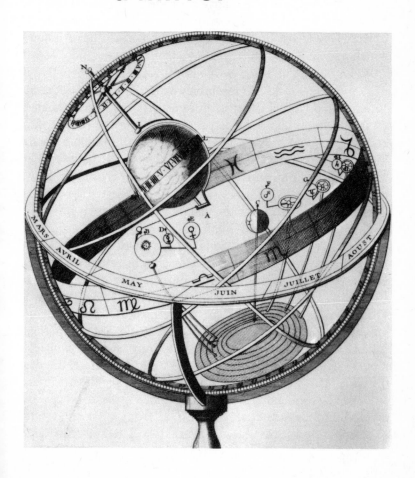

## Reflections in the world

A lake reflects the surrounding landscape, which is blurred
when the wind ruffles the surface of the water and is clearer,
the calmer the lake is. The water's surface acts as a mirror:
objects which are in reality above the surface have images
which appear to be underneath.

When I come up to an ordinary mirror, I see someone in it
who approaches me. He resembles me exactly in every detail.
When I step back a pace, he does exactly the same. A ruler,
12 inches long, if placed perpendicularly on the mirror, has
an image, also 12 inches long, in the mirror, which appears
as a continuation of the real ruler. Each inch on the ruler
corresponds to one on its image. Every point is as far in front
of the mirror as its image is behind, and the distance between
two points is the same as the distance between their images.

There also exist invisible mirrors. It is as if I had a built-in
mirror: a vertical plane through the crown of my head, the
bridge of my nose and the tip of my chin bisects my face, my
skull and my body, the left half being the mirror image of the
right half. But that is not really quite true. My right ear is
somewhat more pointed than my left, and I have a heart
only on the left side, a liver only on the right. Mathematical
solids, however, are often bisected exactly by such invisible
mirrors. Every plane through a cone's axis (figure 7·1) divides
the cone into two halves, each the mirror image of the other.

Depending on how the mirror is placed, the cube can be
divided into right and left (figure 7·2), front and rear (figure
7·3), upper and lower halves (figure 7·4). The halves in each

**Figure 7·1**

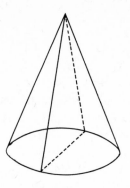

**Figure 7·2**

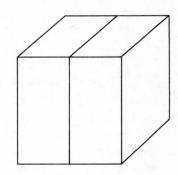

**Figure 7·3**

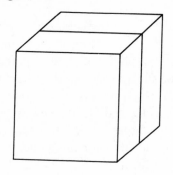

**Figure 7·4**

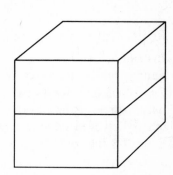

**Figure 7·5**

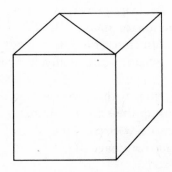

case are the mirror image of each other. The cube can be further divided into two wedges (figure 7·5), each being the mirror image of the other; this can be done in six different ways, corresponding to the six pairs of edges through which the mirror can be made to pass.

Planes dividing a solid into two halves, each of which is the mirror image of the other, are called *planes of symmetry*. The cube has $3 + 6 = 9$ such planes.

## Reflections in the plane

Instead of solids we shall for simplicity consider plane figures, which are easier to draw, such as the 'face' in figure 7·6, which is divided by the dotted line into two mirror image halves, or a regular hexagon, which can be divided into mirror image halves in six ways, three as in figure 7·7 and three as in figure 7·8. The mirror has now contracted to a straight line, the *axis of symmetry*.

We have drawn half of a mirror-symmetric leaf (figure 7·9). How can this figure be completed? Well, from a point $a$ on the edge of the leaf we drop the perpendicular on to the axis of symmetry; $a'$, the mirror image of $a$, lies on this perpendicular, as far behind the mirror as $a$ is in front of it. Repeating this with all points, we can finally join up the mirror images.

This is most easily done with a compass (figure 7·10). Draw a circle about $a$, cutting the axis of symmetry $S$ in $b$ and $c$. With the same radius draw circles about $b$ and $c$ intersecting in $a'$. Then $a'$ is the mirror image of $a$ with respect to $S$. If the

**Figure 7·6**

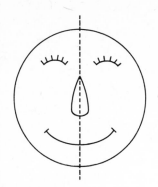

**Figure 7·7**

201

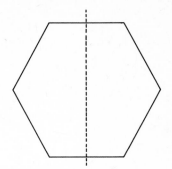

**Figure 7·8**

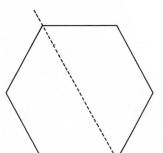

**Figure 7·9**

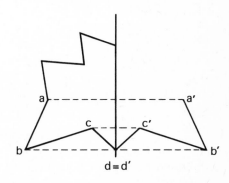

**Figure 7·10**

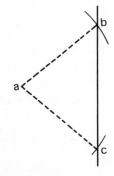

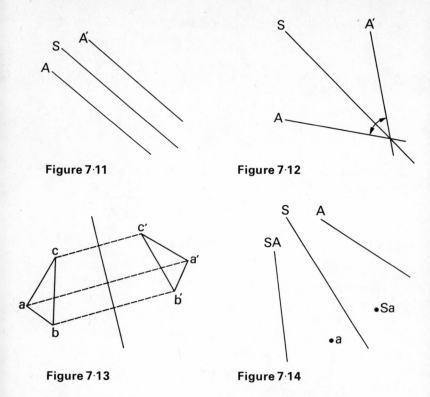

**Figure 7·11**

**Figure 7·12**

**Figure 7·13**

**Figure 7·14**

same construction is started at $a'$, we obtain $a$, which is thus the mirror image of $a'$ with respect to $S$. $a$ and $a'$ are mirror images of each other with respect to $S$.

A point on $S$ coincides with its mirror image. If a straight line $A$ is parallel to $S$, its mirror image is a parallel straight line $A'$ which is as far behind $S$ as $A$ is in front of $S$ (figure 7·11). If the line $A$ meets the axis of reflection $S$ in the point $a$, its mirror image $A'$ does likewise, and they both make the same angle with $S$ (figure 7·12). The mirror image of a triangle $abc$ is a triangle $a'b'c'$ whose sides and angles are equal to the corresponding ones in $abc$ 7·13.

Instead of 'mirror image of the point $a$ with respect to the straight line $S'$ we write simply $Sa$ (figure 7·14); similarly, $SA$ denotes the mirror image of the straight line $A$ under reflection in $S$.

If we reflect twice in $S$, we return to the original point. Thus

$$SSa = a$$
$$SSA = A$$
$$\text{dist}\,(Sa, Sb) = \text{dist}\,(a, b)\,[1]$$
$$\text{angle}\,(SA, SB) = \text{angle}\,(A, B)$$
$$Sa = a \quad \text{if } a \text{ is on } S$$
$$SA = A \text{ if } A = S \text{ or } A \text{ is perpendicular to } S.$$

## Composition of reflections in parallel straight lines

Suppose we reflect first in the straight line $S_1$ and then in the straight line $S_2$. What is the result?

We first assume that $S_1$ and $S_2$ are parallel and a distance $l$ apart (figure 7·15). The perpendiculars from $S_1a$ on to $S_1$ and $S_2$ have a total length of $l$. Now $a$ is as far in front of $S_1$ as $S_1a$ is behind it, and $S_2S_1a$ is as far behind $S_2$ as $S_1a$ is in front of it. Thus $a$ and $S_2S_1a$ are a distance $2l$ apart. The line joining $a$ and $S_2S_1a$ is perpendicular to $S_1$ and $S_2$, and is in the direction from $S_1$ to $S_2$. If I reflect first in $S_1$, then in $S_2$, each point will then be displaced a distance of $2l$ perpendicular to the mirrors, in the direction from $S_1$ to $S_2$.

Actually, we have only shown the above for points $a$ which lie as the $a$ in figure 7·15. However, $a$ could, for example, also

1 dist is an abbreviation for distance.

204

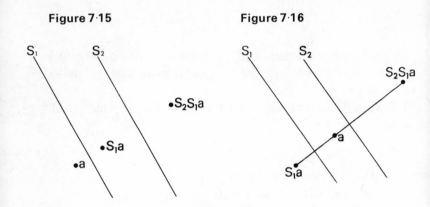

Figure 7·15          Figure 7·16

be situated as in figure 7·16, between $S_1$ and $S_2$, or on the other side of $S_2$. In order to consider the proposition generally, we give the perpendiculars to $S_1$ and $S_2$ the direction from $S_1$ to $S_2$, and regard distances measured in this direction as positive, those measured in the opposite direction as negative. Thus the perpendicular lines from $S_1$ to $S_2$ have positive length $l$.

We now consider these directed distances for a moment. The directed distance from $a$ to $b$ we denote by

$$\overrightarrow{\text{dist}}\,(a, b).$$

Let $a, b, c$ lie on a line perpendicular to $S_1, S_2$. Then we have

$$\overrightarrow{\text{dist}}\,(a, b) + \overrightarrow{\text{dist}}\,(b, c) = \overrightarrow{\text{dist}}\,(a, c),$$

irrespective of the order in which $a, b, c$ lie on the line. Let $a_1, a_2$ be the feet of the perpendiculars from $a$ on to

$S_1, S_2$ respectively. Then

$$\overrightarrow{\text{dist}}\,(a_1, S_1a) + \overrightarrow{\text{dist}}\,(S_1a, a_2) = l,$$

irrespective of $a$'s position. Further

$$\overrightarrow{\text{dist}}\,(a, a_1) = \overrightarrow{\text{dist}}\,(a_1, S_1a)$$
$$\overrightarrow{\text{dist}}\,(S_1a, a_2) = \overrightarrow{\text{dist}}\,(a_2, S_2S_1a).$$

Finally

$$\overrightarrow{\text{dist}}\,(a, S_2S_1a) = \overrightarrow{\text{dist}}\,(a, a_1) + \overrightarrow{\text{dist}}\,(a_1, S_1a) + \overrightarrow{\text{dist}}\,(S_1a, a_2)$$
$$+ \overrightarrow{\text{dist}}\,(a_2, S_2S_1a)$$
$$= 2\,\overrightarrow{\text{dist}}\,(a_1, S_1a) + 2\,\overrightarrow{\text{dist}}\,(S_1a, a_2)$$
$$= 2\,l.$$

It follows that reflection in $S_1$ and then in $S_2$ can be done more simply. From $a$ we draw an arrow, perpendicular to $S_1$ and $S_2$, twice as long as the distance between $S_1$ and $S_2$, and directed from $S_1$ to $S_2$. The tip of the arrow is then $S_2S_1a$.

$S_1S_2a$ is not the same point as $S_2S_1a$, since the former is obtained by drawing the arrow in the opposite direction, from $S_2$ to $S_1$.

If $S_1$ and $S_2$ coincide, their distance apart is zero, the arrows collapse to single points, and thus $S_2S_1a = a$, which we already knew from the end of the previous section.

## Translations

Thus, if we reflect in successive parallel straight lines, we get something new. It is again a mapping, but no longer a

206

**Figure 7·17**

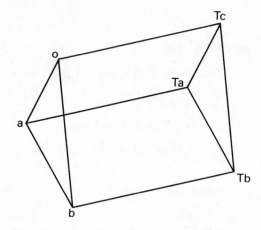

reflection. The arrows from a point to its image are all parallel, equal in length and in the same direction. This is called a displacement or *translation*. The image of $a, b, \ldots$ under such a translation we call $Ta, Tb, \ldots$ (figure 7·17). All arrows $(a, Ta)$ etc. are parallel, equally long and in the same direction. It further follows that $(a, b)$ and $(Ta, Tb)$ are also parallel and of the same length. A translation moves every straight line parallel to itself.

If two reflections in parallel straight lines are combined, we get a translation

$$S_2 S_1 a = Ta.$$

This is also the case when $S_1$, $S_2$ coincide. The translation arrow has then zero length, and the translation leaves each point fixed. The translation obtained by combining $S_1$ and $S_2$ we denote also by $S_2 S_1$, the *product* of $S_2$ and $S_1$.

A translation $T$ is completely determined, if any one of its translation arrows $(a, Ta)$ is known. To construct $Tb$ one has

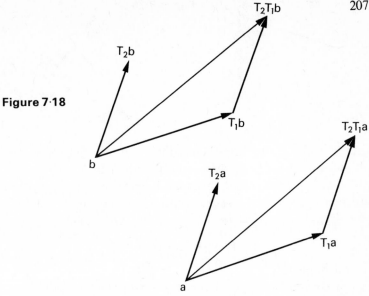

**Figure 7·18**

simply to move the arrow to *b*, keeping its direction fixed.

Given any arrow, I can also always construct a translation of which it is a translation arrow: I draw two lines perpendicular to the arrow, separated by half the arrow's length, and call them $S_1$, $S_2$, where $S_1$, $S_2$ follow each other in the arrow's direction. Then $S_2S_1$ is a translation with the required arrow. In drawing the lines $S_1$, $S_2$ I can choose one of them as I please so long as it is perpendicular to the arrow.

Now, what happens when two translations $T_1$ and $T_2$ are carried out, one after the other? I first have to subject *a* to the translation $T_1$, giving $T_1a$. Then I subject $T_1a$ to the translation $T_2$; I must thus move the arrow ($a$, $T_2a$) parallel to itself to $T_1a$. Thus $T_2T_1a$ is obtained (figure 7·18). If I want to construct $T_2T_1b$, I must first move the arrow ($a$, $T_1a$) to *b*, and then the arrow ($a$, $T_2a$) to $T_1b$. This has the same result as if I move the figure *a*, $T_1a$, $T_2T_1a$ as a whole to *b*. Thus the arrows ($a$, $T_2T_1a$) and ($b$, $T_2T_1b$) are also parallel, equal in

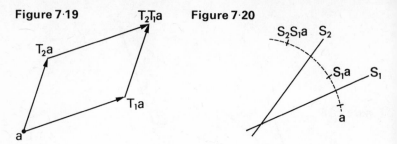

**Figure 7·19**

$T_2a$

$T_2T_1a$

$T_1a$

$a$

**Figure 7·20**

$S_2S_1a$   $S_2$

$S_1a$   $S_1$

$a$

length and in the same direction. For all points $x$, the arrows $(x, T_2T_1x)$ are thus parallel, equal in length and in the same direction, and this means that the composition of the two translations $T_1T_2$ is again a translation. We denote it by $T_2T_1$ and thus write

$$(T_2T_1)a = T_2T_1a$$

for all points $a$.

The composition or *product* of two translations is obtained by composing the translation arrows. Figure 7·19 shows that the order in which they are composed is unimportant; it does not matter whether I move the arrow $(a, T_2a)$ to $T_1a$ or the arrow $(a, T_1a)$ to $T_2a$. The construction gives the same result for $T_2T_1a$ and $T_1T_2a$. $T_2T_1$ and $T_1T_2$ are the same translation:

$$T_1T_2 = T_2T_1.$$

(It was different with reflections.)

## Composition of reflections in intersecting straight lines

We now assume that the straight lines $S_1$, $S_2$ intersect in $z$ (figure 7·20), and reflect first in $S_1$, then in $S_2$. The point of intersection $z$ remains fixed at each stage. Thus

$$S_2S_1z = z.$$

Further, all distances remain constant under both reflections; thus

$$\text{dist } (S_2S_1a, S_2S_1b) = \text{dist } (a, b).$$

In particular, the distances from $z$ remain the same,

$$\text{dist } (S_2S_1a, z) = \text{dist } (a, z).$$

Thus $a$ and $S_2S_1a$ lie on a circle, centre $z$.

Each point of the plane is rotated about $z$, all distances between points of the plane remaining fixed. The plane is rotated like a solid body about the point $z$. We call the result of this movement a *turning* or rotation $R$ about $z$. It has been obtained by reflecting consecutively in $S_1$ and $S_2$, and we denote it by

$$R = S_2S_1,$$

the *product* of the reflections in $S_1$ and $S_2$.

The only question is, how much is the plane rotated. How should we measure this?

Draw two arrows starting from $z$, with tips $a$, $b$ respectively. We now wish to define the angle between the two arrows, not the ordinary angle, but the directed one.

We suppose the first arrow rotated to the left (anticlockwise) into the second. The angle it describes we call

$$\measuredangle \ (za, zb) \qquad \text{(figure 7·21)}.$$

The order of the arrows is important. If $\measuredangle \ (za, zb) = a$, as in figure 7·22, then the angle $\measuredangle \ (zb, za)$ is $360° - a$, or, since with angles multiples of $360°$ are of no consequence, $-a$.

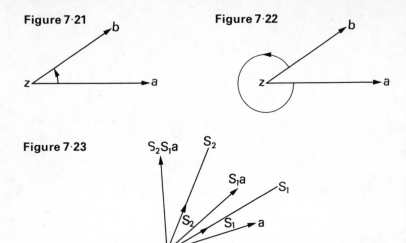

Figure 7·21

Figure 7·22

Figure 7·23

$S_2S_1a$  $S_2$

$S_1a$  $S_1$

$S_2$  $S_1$  a

z

Given three arrows from $z$ with tips $a, b, c$, we always have

$$\angle (za, zb) + \angle (zb, zc) = \angle (za, zc),$$

provided due attention is paid to the sign of the angles.

We return to the reflections in $S_1$ and $S_2$ (figure 7·23). We take points $s_1, s_2$ different from $z$ on $S_1, S_2$ respectively. The arrows $zs_1, zs_2$ make an angle $\varphi$. We also draw the arrows from $z$ to $a$, $S_1a$ and $S_2S_1a$. We are interested in the angle $\angle (za, zS_2S_1a)$. This is

$$\angle (za, zS_1a) + \angle (zS_1a, zS_2S_1a)$$
$$= 2 \angle (zs_1, zS_1a) + 2 \angle (zS_1a, zs_2)$$
$$= 2 \varphi.$$

Thus: *under the rotation* $R = S_2S_1$, *each point remains on its circle about* z, *and is in fact rotated through twice the angle which an arrow on* $S_1$ *makes with one on* $S_2$.

(The angle $\varphi$ is in fact not uniquely determined. If, for

Figure 7·24

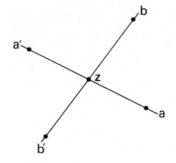

example $s_2$ is replaced by a point on $S_2$, on the other side from $z$, $\varphi$ becomes $\varphi + 180°$. But this does not fundamentally alter $2\varphi$, since we have added $360°$, which does not affect matters anyway.)

The order in which $S_1$ and $S_2$ are taken is important in forming their product. If they are interchanged, $\varphi$ becomes $-\varphi$ and so $2\varphi$ becomes $-2\varphi$. The product is thus a rotation through the reversed angle. $2\varphi$ and $-2\varphi$ only represent the same angle if $2\varphi = 0°$ or $180°$, i.e. $\varphi = 0°$ or $90°$. Thus

$$S_1S_2 = S_2S_1$$

only if the straight lines $S_1$ and $S_2$ coincide or are perpendicular to each other. If $S_1$, $S_2$ coincide, $S_2S_1$ is the rotation through $0°$, which leaves each point fixed. If $S_1$, $S_2$ are perpendicular to each other, $S_2S_1$ is a rotation through $180°$, also called a *point reflection* in $z$: $z$ is the midpoint of the line joining a point to its image (figure 7·24).

A rotation $R$ is determined by the centre of rotation $z$,

about which the rotation takes place, and by the *angle of rotation*. A given rotation $R$ can be expressed as the product of reflections in straight lines $S_1$, $S_2$ which pass through $z$. $S_1$ can be any line passing through $z$, and we have only to make sure that $S_1$ and $S_2$ intersect in $z$ at an angle equal to half the given angle of rotation.

## Composition of rotations

We consider two rotations $R_1$, $R_2$ with centres of rotation $z_1$, $z_2$ and angles of rotation $\varphi_1$, $\varphi_2$ respectively. We wish to compose them, i.e. carry out first $R_1$ and then $R_2$. What do we get?

We can represent $R_1$ as a product of two reflections

$$R_1 = S_2 S_1$$

and similarly

$$R_2 = S_4 S_3.$$

In doing this we can specify for $S_2$ an arbitrary line through $z_1$ and similarly for $S_3$ an arbitrary line through $z_2$. In fact, we take $S_2 = S_3$, i.e. we take the straight line joining $z_1$ and $z_2$, if the points are different, and any line through $z_1 = z_2$ if they coincide. In

$$R_2 R_1 = S_4 S_3 S_2 S_1$$

$S_3$ and $S_2$, which are equal, are adjacent. We thus reflect twice consecutively in the same straight line. This has no effect. We can omit $S_3 S_2$ from the product and get

$$R_2 R_1 = S_4 S_1.$$

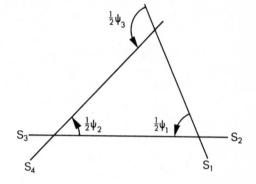

**Figure 7·25**

$R_2R_1$ is thus also the product of two reflections and is hence either a rotation or a translation. What it in fact is depends on the angles of rotation $\varphi_1$, $\varphi_2$, and this can be seen at once.

First of all, $S_1$, $S_4$ can be parallel (or equal). Then $R_2R_1$ $= S_4S_1$ is a translation. Or, on the other hand, $S_1$, $S_4$ are not parallel. Then we have (figure 7·25) a rotation about the point of intersection of $S_1$ and $S_4$ with angle of rotation $\varphi_3$. By the theorem on the exterior angle of a triangle we have

$$\tfrac{1}{2}\psi_3 = \tfrac{1}{2}\psi_1 + \tfrac{1}{2}\psi_2, \text{ hence } \psi_3 = \psi_1 + \psi_2.$$

$\psi_1 + \psi_2 = 0$ occurs only when $\tfrac{1}{2}\psi_1 + \tfrac{1}{2}\psi_2 = 0°$ or $180°$, and this means that $S_1$ and $S_4$ are parallel, i.e. that $R_2R_1$ is a translation.

To sum up:

*The product of two rotations with angles of rotation $\psi_1$, $\psi_2$ is a rotation with the angle of rotation $\psi_1 + \psi_2$, if the latter is not $0°$, and a translation if it is $0°$.*

(It can of course also be the translation which leaves everything fixed; one can also regard it as a rotation.)

If $R_2R_1$ is a rotation, so is $R_1R_2$, with the same angle of rotation, which is simply the sum of the two, but the two centres of rotation can be different.

If $R_1$, $R_2$ are rotations with the same centre of rotation, $R_1R_2$ and $R_2R_1$ have the same centre of rotation (and angle of rotation), and are thus identical.

If $R_2R_1$ is a translation, so is $R_1R_2$ (since if $\psi_1 + \psi_2 = 0$, then $\psi_2 + \psi_1 = 0$) and in general they are not the same.

## Composition of a rotation and a translation

Let the rotation be $R$, the translation $T$. Let the rotation $R$ have the centre of rotation $z$ and the angle of rotation $\psi \neq 0$. Denote by $S_2$ the straight line through $z$ perpendicular to the translation arrow of $T$. We then can choose $S_1$ so that

$$R = S_2S_1.$$

Write the translation $T$ also as a product of two reflections.

$$T = S_4S_3.$$

In doing so, we choose $S_3 = S_2$. Then we need only take $S_4$ parallel to $S_3$ and at a distance from it of half the translation arrow (figure 7·26). In

$$TR = S_4S_3S_2S_1$$

$S_3S_2$ can again be omitted. Thus

$$TR = S_4S_1.$$

Figure 7·26

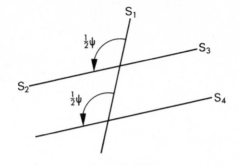

Since $S_4$ is parallel to $S_3 = S_2$ and $S_2$, $S_1$ intersect (in $z$), $S_4$ and $S_1$ are certainly not parallel or equal; thus $S_4 S_1 = TR$ is a rotation and in fact with the same angle of rotation as $R$ (but with a different centre of rotation).

Similar results can be obtained for $RT$.

To sum up:

*The product of a rotation and a translation (or vice versa) is a rotation with the same angle of rotation.*

## Arbitrary products of reflections

With the straight lines $S_1$, $S_2$, $S_3$, $S_4$ one can form the product

$$S_4 S_3 S_2 S_1$$

of reflections. Now, by our previous findings $S_2 S_1$ and $S_4 S_3$ are each a translation or a rotation; their product is again a translation or rotation, and thus can be written as a product of two reflections.

So each product of four reflections can be written as a product of two reflections.

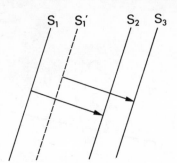

**Figure 7·27**

We now consider a product of five reflections

$$S_5 S_4 S_3 S_2 S_1.$$

Since $S_4 S_3 S_2 S_1$ can be written as a product of two reflections, the whole can be represented as a product of three reflections.

Similarly with more factors. A product of an even number of reflections can be written in the simplest way as a product of two or no reflections (the latter is the mapping which leaves all points fixed); a product of an odd number of reflections can be written in the simplest way as a product of reflections with three factors or one factor (the latter is simply a reflection).

We examine the products

$$S_3 S_2 S_1$$

more closely.

First of all, let $S_2$ be parallel to both $S_3$ and $S_1$ (figure 7·27). $S_2 S_1$ is then a translation. We get the same translation if we replace $S_1$, $S_2$ by parallel straight lines $S_1'$, $S_2'$, so that the arrow from $S_1$ to $S_2$ and the one from $S_1'$ to $S_2'$ are equal and in the same direction. In doing this we can choose $S_2' = S_3$. Then

$$S_3 S_2 S_1 = S_3 S_2' S_1' = S_1',$$

and is thus a reflection.

**Figure 7·28a**          **Figure 7·28b**

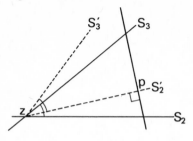
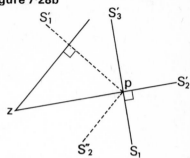

Now let $S_2$ not be parallel to $S_3$ (figure 7·28a), and their point of intersection be $z$, the centre of rotation of the rotation $S_3S_2$. We get the same rotation if we replace $S_2$, $S_3$ by straight lines $S_2'$, $S_3'$, which intersect in $z$ at the same angle as $S_2$, $S_3$. In doing this we wish to choose $S_2'$ perpendicular to $S_1$. In

$$S_3S_2S_1 = S_3'S_2'S_1$$

consider now $S_2'S_1$. The straight lines $S_1$, $S_2'$ intersect perpendicularly in $p$. Thus $S_2'S_1$ is a point reflection in $p$. We get the same if we replace $S_1$, $S_2'$ by two other straight lines $S_1'$, $S_2''$ which intersect perpendicularly in $p$ (figure 7·28b). In doing this we may choose $S_1'$ perpendicular to $S_3'$. Then

$$S_3S_2S_1 = S_3'S_2'S_1 = S_3'S_2''S_1'$$

with $S_1'$ perpendicular to $S_2''$ and $S_3'$. Thus $S_2''$ and $S_3'$ are parallel. Now

$$T = S_3'S_2''$$

is a translation, and (with $S$ instead of $S_1'$)

$$S_3S_2S_1 = TS$$

is the product of a reflection and a translation, whose arrows are parallel to the axis of reflection $S$ (figure 7·29). This is called a *glide reflection*. We note furthermore that in

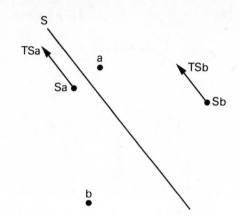

**Figure 7·29**

this case $TS = ST$. The reflection in a straight line is a special case of glide reflection, namely with a vanishing translation arrow.

We have assumed that $S_2$ is not parallel to $S_3$. If, however, $S_2$ is parallel to $S_3$, we may assume that $S_2$ is not parallel to $S_1$, since the case of $S_2$ parallel to both has already been done. We finish in an exactly analogous way and reach the same result as immediately above.

To sum up:

*The product of an even number of reflections is a translation or a rotation, that of an odd number is a glide reflection.*

## Mappings

Reflections, translations, rotations and glide reflections are special cases of mappings. In general, one talks of a *mapping* of the plane into itself if with each point of the plane is associated a point as image.

The following also exemplifies mapping of the plane:

A fixed point $p$ is taken. The image point $a'$ of a point $a$

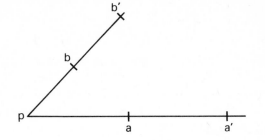

is defined as lying on the continuation of *pa* beyond *a*, twice as far from *p* as *a* is (figure 7·30).

This mapping is called a dilatation relative to *p* by the factor 2.

Instead of 2, any other number can be chosen, even a negative one – in that case, one would have to seek *a'* on the other side of *p* on the straight line *pa*.

Under a dilatation by *m*, all distances in the plane are multiplied by the absolute value of *m*.

In this sense, one can also talk about dilation relative to *p* by the factor 0. Under this, each point is mapped on to *p*; the whole plane is the 'inverse image' of *p*. Under the other mappings, each point had exactly one inverse image, i.e. corresponding to each point there was exactly one point whose image it was. Such mappings can be inverted: if, under a mapping, *a'* is the image of *a*, then, under the inverse mapping, *a* is the image of *a'*. The inverse of a dilation relative to *p* by the factor 2 is a dilation relative to *p* by the factor $\frac{1}{2}$. The inverse of a translation is the translation with reversed translation arrow. The inverse of a rotation with centre of rotation *z* and angle of rotation $\psi$ is a rotation with centre of rotation *z* and angle of rotation $-\psi$. The inverse of the reflection in the straight line $S$ is this same reflection, the inverse of a glide reflection is a glide reflection. If I carry out a mapping and then its inverse, nothing has changed. Together they give the mapping under which each point is its own image point, the *identity mapping*.

We shall in general denote mappings by capital letters, and the identity mapping in particular by $I$. If $F$ is such a mapping, and $a$ is a point of the plane, then its image point is called $Fa$. Thus in particular $Ia = a$ for all $a$.

The inverse of the mapping $F$ (if $F$ is invertible, i.e. if each point is the image of exactly one point) is called $F^{-1}$. The inverse of the inverse of $F$ is $F$ itself, i.e. $(F^{-1})^{-1} = F$.

Let two mappings $F_1, F_2$ be given. I first carry out $F_1$ and then $F_2$. A point $a$ then goes first into $F_1a$ which then becomes $F_2F_1a$. A new mapping is obtained, under which each point $a$ has the image $F_2F_1a$. We call this mapping $F_2F_1$, the *product* of $F_1$ and $F_2$. Thus

$$(F_2F_1)a = F_2F_1a.$$

We saw already that

$$F^{-1}F = FF^{-1} = I.$$

## Groups

We saw that the product of two translations is again a translation, and that the same is true of the inverse of a translation. This property is usually expressed as follows: the translations form a *group*.

We consider the rotations with fixed centre of rotation $z$. The product of two rotations and the inverse of a rotation are again rotations with centre of rotation $z$. The rotations with centre of rotation $z$ form a group.

Let us now look at all possible products of reflections (including the product with 0 factors, the mapping $I$). They also form a group. The product of two products of reflections is again a product of reflections. The inverse of the product $S_n S_{n-1} \ldots S_2 S_1$ of reflections is $S_1 S_2 \ldots S_{n-1} S_n$, since

$$
\begin{aligned}
&S_1 S_2 \ldots S_{n-1} S_n S_n S_{n-1} \ldots S_2 S_1 \\
&= S_1 S_2 \ldots S_{n-1} S_{n-1} \ldots S_2 S_1 \\
&= S_1 S_2 \ldots \quad \ldots S_2 S_1 \\
&= \ldots \\
&= S_1 S_2 S_2 S_1 \\
&= S_1 S_1 \\
&= I.
\end{aligned}
$$

In any case, the inverse of a product of reflections is again a product of reflections.

The reflections by themselves do not, of course, form a group, since the product of two reflections is not a reflection.

In general, one understands by a *group* of mappings of the plane a system $\Sigma$ of mappings such that if $F_1$, $F_2$ belong to the system $\Sigma$, so do $F_2 F_1$ and $F_1^{-1}$. A sub-system $\Sigma'$ of a group $\Sigma$ which again forms a group is called a *subgroup* of $\Sigma$.

In the group consisting of products of all reflections the translations form a subgroup. Also the products with an even number of factors form a subgroup.

## Congruences

A mapping of the plane, under which distances are not altered, is called a *congruence*. Under a congruence the plane behaves so to speak like a solid body; each figure goes into a congruent one; straight lines go into straight lines, circles into circles. We can also express the fact that $F$ is a congruence as follows:

$$\text{dist } (Fa, Fb) = \text{dist } (a, b)$$

for all pairs of points $a, b$.

The congruences form a group, since if

$$\text{dist } (F_1 a, F_1 b) = \text{dist } (a, b),$$
$$\text{dist } (F_2 a, F_2 b) = \text{dist } (a, b),$$

then    $$\text{dist } (F_2 F_1 a, F_2 F_1 b) = \text{dist } (F_1 a, F_1 b)$$
$$= \text{dist } (a, b)$$

and    $$\text{dist } (F_1^{-1} a, F_1^{-1} b) = \text{dist } (F_1 F_1^{-1} a, F_1 F_1^{-1} b)$$
$$= \text{dist } (a, b).$$

Let $a, b$ be two distinct points and $F$ a congruence which leaves them fixed,

$$Fa = a, Fb = b.$$

Then for each point $x$ (see figure 7·31)

$$\text{dist } (Fx, a) = \text{dist } (Fx, Fa) = \text{dist } (x, a),$$
$$\text{dist } (Fx, b) = \text{dist } (Fx, Fb) = \text{dist } (x, b).$$

$Fx$ thus has the same distances from $a$ and $b$ respectively as $x$. But there are at most two points having the given distances from $a$ and $b$, and they are the mirror images of each other.

**Figure 7·31**                                                   223

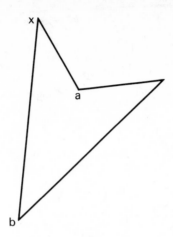

Thus, if the congruence $F$ leaves the distinct points $a, b$ fixed, we have for each point $x$

either $Fx = x$

or  $Fx = $ mirror image of $x$ with respect to the straight line $ab$.

$F$ could leave all points fixed, i.e.

$F = I.$

If this is not the case, there is a point $c$ which is distinct from $Fc$. Let $x$ be a point with $Fx = x$. Then

$$\text{dist } (x, c) = \text{dist } (Fx, Fc) = \text{dist } (x, Fc),$$

i.e. $x$ lies on the perpendicular bisector of $c, Fc$, and that is the straight line $ab$. The points $x$ not on the straight line $ab$ thus do not remain fixed; for them it is true that $Fx$ is different from $x$, thus $Fx$ is the mirror image of $x$ with respect to the straight line $ab$. This always holds for the points on $ab$, too.

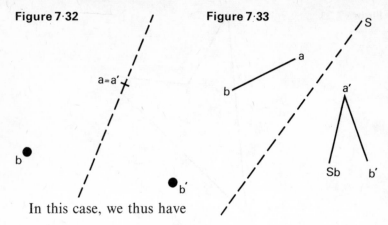

Figure 7·32          Figure 7·33

In this case, we thus have

$$F = \text{reflection in } ab.$$

It has been shown that:

*A congruence which leaves the distinct points $a, b$ fixed is either* I *or the reflection in the straight line* $ab$.

We now consider two pairs of points $a, b$ and $a', b'$ with the same distance between them, i.e.

$$\text{dist } (a, b) = \text{dist } (a', b').$$

We show that there are exactly two congruences $F$ which carry $a, b$ into $a', b'$ respectively, and so satisfy

$$Fa = a', \quad Fb = b'.$$

If $a = a'$, $b = b'$, I is one such required congruence. If $a = a'$ and $b \neq b'$ (figure 7·32), the perpendicular bisector of $bb'$ passes through $a$; the reflection in the perpendicular bisector gives a congruence as required. Let $a \neq a'$ (figure 7·33). We then reflect first of all in the perpendicular bisector $S$ of $aa'$. Then

$$a' = Sa$$

and dist $(a', b') = \text{dist } (a, b) = \text{dist } (Sa, Sb) = \text{dist } (a', Sb)$.

The pairs of points $a'$, $Sb$ and $a'$, $b'$ belong to one of the previous cases. There is thus a congruence $F_0$ which carries $a'$, $Sb$ into $a'$, $b'$ respectively.

$$F_0 a' = a', \; F_0 Sb = b'.$$

Since $a' = Sa$, we have

$$F_0 Sa = a', \; F_0 Sb = b'$$

and the product $F = F_0 S$ gives the required congruence.

We have thus found a congruence $F$ which carries $a, b$ into $a', b'$ respectively. I find another one if I now further reflect in the straight line $S'$ joining $a'$ and $b'$. $S'F$ also carries $a, b$ into $a', b'$ respectively. Both $F$ and $SF$ are products of reflections.

But this is all. Let $F$ and $F_1$ be both so obtained that they carry $a$, $b$ into $a'$, $b'$ respectively, i.e.

$$Fa = F_1 a = a', \; Fb = F_1 b = b'.$$

Then $F^{-1}$ is also a congruence and

$$F^{-1}a' = a, \; F^{-1}b' = b,$$
$$\text{so } F_1 F^{-1} a' = a', \; F_1 F^{-1} b' = b'.$$

The congruence $F_1 F^{-1}$ leaves the distinct points $a'$, $b'$ fixed, and is then, by what has been done before, either $I$ or the reflection in $S'$. Thus

$$F_1 F^{-1} = I \;\; \text{or} = S',$$
$$F_1 F^{-1} F = IF \text{ or} = S'F,$$
$$F_1 = F \;\; \text{or} = S'F.$$

226

It has been shown that

*corresponding to two pairs of points* a, b *and* a′, b′ *with*

$$dist\ (a, b) = dist\ (a', b') \neq 0$$

*there are exactly two congruences which carry* a, b *into* a′, b′ *respectively; both can be obtained as products of reflections; they differ by one reflection.*

From this it also follows that

*every congruence can be expressed as a product of reflections.*

We now take three non-collinear points $a$, $b$, $c$ and three points $a′$, $b′$ $c′$ with the same respective distances apart, i.e.

$$\text{dist } (a, b) = \text{dist } (a', b'),$$
$$\text{dist } (b, c) = \text{dist } (b', c'),$$
$$\text{dist } (c, a) = \text{dist } (c', a').$$

We shall then find exactly one congruence which carries $a$, $b$, $c$ into $a′$, $b′$, $c′$.

In any case, there is a congruence $F_0$ with

$$F_0 a = a', \ F_0 b = b'.$$

$$\text{Dist } (F_0 c, a') = \text{dist } (F_0 c, F_0 a) = \text{dist } (c, a)$$
$$= \text{dist } (c', a'),$$
$$\text{thus } \text{ dist } (F_0 c, a') = \text{dist } (c', a').$$
$$\text{Similarly, dist } (F_0 c, b') = \text{dist } (c', b').$$

$F_0 c$ is as far from $a′$, $b′$ respectively as is $c′$. Thus either $F_0 c = c′$ or $F_0 c$ and $c′$ are mirror images of each other with respect to the straight line $a′b′$. In the first case, the required congruence is given by $F = F_0$, in the second case, by $F = SF_0$, where $S$ is the straight line $a′b′$.

If $F$ and $F_1$ are congruences which carry $a$, $b$, $c$ into

$a'$, $b'$, $c'$ respectively, $F^{-1}F_1$ is a congruence which leaves $a, b, c$ fixed and is thus either $I$ or the reflection in the straight line $ab$. The latter is impossible, since $F^{-1}F_1$ leaves the point $c$ fixed, while $c$ certainly does not lie on the straight line $ab$. Thus $F^{-1}F_1 = I$, i.e. $F_1 = F$.

We have seen that

*there is exactly one congruence which carries the non-collinear points* a, b, c *into the points* a′, b′, c′ *with the same corresponding distances.*

To sum up:

Theorem: *The congruences form a group. The products of reflections form the same group. Each congruence can be obtained as a product of 0, 1, 2 or 3 reflections. If* a, b, c *are not collinear and* a′, b′, c′ *have the same corresponding distances, there are exactly two congruences which carry* a, b *into* a′, b′ *respectively* (*they differ by one reflection*) *and exactly one which carries* a, b, c *into* a′, b′, c′ *respectively.*

## Displacements

We consider more closely those congruences which are products of an even number (0 or 2) of reflections. We call them *displacements*. Each displacement is, as we saw, a translation or a rotation, and vice versa. The displacements form a group, a subgroup of the group of congruences.

Is it possible to see directly whether a congruence is a displacement, i.e. without decomposing it into reflections?

Under a reflection distances remain fixed. Also angles in the usual sense do not change. On p. 219, however, we intro-

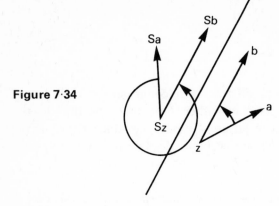

**Figure 7·34**

duced a more subtle concept of angle. Under reflection in $S$ $\not\prec$ $(za, zb)$ goes into $\not\prec'$ $(Sz\, Sa, Sz\, Sb)$ (figure 7·34). The image angle is not equal to the original one, but is its reverse. After two reflections the image angle is again equal to the original one, after three it is reversed.

We thus have:

Theorem: *Congruences preserve distances. Under a congruence all angles remain the same or go into the reversed angle. The displacements are distinguished among the congruences in that they also preserve angles.*

It is because of this property that we speak of displacements. A translation or rotation can be carried out gradually, a reflection or glide reflection cannot, since an angle can only go suddenly into the reversed one.

## In three dimensions

In three dimensions, some things are exactly as in the plane, some are more complicated. We deal briefly with what remains the same.

We now reflect in planes, for which we use the symbols $S$, $S_1$, etc.

If $S_1$, $S_2$ are parallel, $S_2 S_1$ is again a translation, this time of space; for all $x$, the arrows from $x$ to $S_2 S_1 x$ are again parallel, equal in length and in the same direction; all translations are obtainable in this way. The translations again form a group and each pair of translations $T_1$, $T_2$ satisfy

$$T_1 T_2 = T_2 T_1.$$

If $S_1$, $S_2$ are not parallel, $S_2 S_1$ is a rotation with the line of intersection of $S_1$, $S_2$ as axis of rotation and twice the angle between $S_1$, $S_2$ as angle of rotation. $S_1 S_2 = S_2 S_1$ if and only if $S_1 = S_2$ or $S_1$ is perpendicular to $S_2$; in the first case $S_1 S_2 = I$, in the second $S_1 S_2$ is a reflection in the line of intersection of $S_1$ and $S_2$.

The mappings of space which preserve distances are called *congruences*. They form a group. The reflections are congruences, the products of reflections are, too, and they form a group which is contained in the group of congruences. Theorem: *The congruences form a group, the products of reflections form the same group. Each congruence can be represented as a product of at most four reflections. If* a, b, c, d *are not coplanar and* a′, b′, c′, d′ *are the same corresponding distances apart, there are exactly two congruences which carry* a, b, c *into* a′, b′, c′ *respectively* (*they differ by one reflection*) *and exactly one which carries* a, b, c, d *into* a′, b′, c′, d′ *respectively.*

This theorem is proved like the corresponding one for the plane. The points $a$, $b$, $c$, $d$ are brought consecutively to the desired spot by at the most four reflections. If $a$, $b$, $c$ are positioned, there are still two possibilities for the last one.

How should one define the displacements of space? The products of an even number of reflections certainly form a group. But is this also a proper subgroup? A congruence can of course be represented as a product of reflections in many ways, and it would be conceivable that each one which can be represented as a product of an odd number is also representable as a product of an even number. In the plane we could dismiss this possibility: angles were preserved under an even number of reflections, reversed under an odd number. By their effect on angles both forms were cleanly distinguished. Unfortunately, this is no longer true for the angle between two planes: reflection in the plane bisecting the angle reverses it while reflection in a plane perpendicular to the line of intersection preserves it.

We adopt another approach.

First, a preliminary remark: if $S_1$, $S_2$, $S_3$ are parallel planes, there is a plane $S_4$, parallel to them, such that

$$S_4 S_3 = S_2 S_1.$$

I have only to make sure that $S_3$, $S_4$ follow each other at the same distance and in the same direction as $S_1$, $S_2$. Similarly, if $S_1$, $S_2$, $S_3$ pass through the same straight line, there is a plane $S_4$ through the same straight line such that

$$S_4 S_3 = S_2 S_1.$$

I have only to make sure that $S_4$ makes the same angle with $S_3$ as does $S_2$ with $S_1$.

We combine both cases. We understand by a pencil either the system of all planes which are parallel to one plane or the system of all planes which pass through a fixed straight line. Note that any two planes determine a pencil. Then we have:

If the planes $S_1$, $S_2$, $S_3$ belong to a pencil, there is a plane $S_4$ in the same pencil such that

$$S_4 S_3 = S_2 S_1.$$

We further note that

$$S_1 S_2 = S_2 S_1$$

whenever $S_1$, $S_2$ are perpendicular to each other.

Now let

$$F = S_m S_{m-1} \ldots S_2 S_1$$

be expressed as a product of reflections. We shall modify the representation, the number of factors, however, remaining the same. (Naturally, $F$ itself remains the same too, only the representation is changed.)

Take a point $a$. In the pencil of $S_1$, $S_2$ there is a plane $S_1'$ which passes through $a$. Let $S_2'$ be determined so that

$$S_2' S_1' = S_2 S_1$$

and replace $S_2 S_1$ in the expression for $F$ by $S_2' S_1'$. Thus

$$F = S_m S_{m-1} \ldots S_3 S_2' S_1'.$$

Proceed similarly with the pencil of $S_2'$, $S_3$; seek a plane $S_2''$ there which contains $a$, and define $S_3'$ so that

$$S_3' S_2'' = S_3 S_2'.$$

Substitute again,

$$F = S_m S_{m-1} \ldots S_3' S_2'' S_1'.$$

And so on. We finally get a representation

$$F = S_m' S_{m-1}'' \ldots S_3'' S_2'' S_1', \qquad (1)$$

where all planes except possibly $S_m'$ contain the point $a$.

Now repeat this with a point $b$ ($\neq a$) and obtain a representation of $F$ in which all except the last one still contain $a$ and, furthermore, all except the last two contain $b$. Repeat this again with a point $c$ (not on the straight line $ab$).

It leads to a representation

$$F = S_m^* S_{m-1}^* \ldots S_2^* S_1^*,$$

where $a$ lies on $S_1^*, \ldots S_{m-1}^*$, $b$ lies on $S_1^*, \ldots S_{m-2}^*$, $c$ lies on $S_1^*, \ldots S_{m-3}^*$. All planes $S_1^*, \ldots S_{m-3}^*$ contain $a, b, c$ and thus are identical, $S_{m-3}^* \ldots S_1^* = I$ or $S_1^*$, from which it again follows that we can manage with at most four factors.

Now let

$$F = I, \text{ say.}$$

In representation (1), all planes, except perhaps $S'_m$, contained the point $a$

$$a = Ia = Fa = S_m' S_{m-1}'' \ldots S_2'' S_1' a = S_m' a,$$

thus the plane $S_m'$ contains the point $a$, too.

Repeating the step by step substitution, now with $b$, we get a representation where all planes contain $a$ and all, except perhaps the last, contain $b$. As just previously, we conclude from $b = Ib = Fb$ that also the last one contains $b$. Again with $c$ we finally get a representation like (2), now with $a, b, c$ on all the planes $S_1^*, \ldots, S_m^*$, which thus coincide,

$$I = S_1^* \ldots S_1^* \quad (m \text{ factors}),$$

from which it follows that $m$ must be even.

Thus, in each representation of $I$ as a product of reflections the number of factors is even.

Now let any congruence $F$ be represented in two ways as a product of reflections,

$$F = S_k \ldots S_1 = S_l' \ldots S_1'.$$

Then

$$I = F^{-1}F = S_1 \ldots S_k S_l' \ldots S_1'.$$

Thus $k + l$ is even, i.e. $k, l$ are both even or both odd.

It has been shown that

*Whether a congruence can be expressed as a product of an even or odd number of reflections does not depend on the way in which it is represented.*

We call products of an *even number* of reflections *displacements*.

The displacements form a group. A displacement can be written as a product of an even number of reflections (0, 2, 4 in the shortest form). The products of an odd number of reflections are not displacements.

We now wish to examine the congruences more closely. We first take those which leave a certain point $a$ fixed.

$$Fa = a,$$
$$F = S_m \ldots S_1.$$

We again carry through the substitutions with this $a$ and obtain representation (1), where all the planes except perhaps $S'_m$ contain the point $a$. We again conclude from $Fa = a$ that $a$ also lies on $S'_m$.

Repeating the process with $b$ and $c$ (where $a$, $b$, $c$ should not be collinear) we get representation (2), only now $a$ lies on $S_1^*, \ldots, S_m^*$, $b$ on $S_1^*, \ldots, S_{m-1}^*$, $c$ on $S_1^*, \ldots, S_{m-2}^*$. $S_1^*, \ldots, S_{m-2}^*$ are now the same plane. According as $m$ is even or odd

$$S_{m-2}^* \ldots S_1^* = I \text{ or } S_1^*.$$

Representation (2) is thus reduced to one with three factors for $m$ odd and with two factors for $m$ even. Thus: *Let* F *be a congruence with the fixed point* a. *Then* F *can be written as a product of two or three reflections in planes which contain the point* a.

The *displacements with a fixed point* are thus products of two reflections, i.e. *rotations* ($I$ included).

We consider an arbitrary displacement $F$ which should not be simply a translation or a rotation. Let $a$ be some point. There is a translation $T$ which carries $a$ into $Fa$, i.e.

$$Ta = Fa,$$
$$T^{-1}Fa = a.$$

Since $T^{-1}F$ leaves the point $a$ fixed, by the above, $T^{-1}F$ is a rotation $R$, i.e.

$$F = TR,$$

a product of a rotation and a translation.

We break down the translation arrow into a component parallel to the axis of rotation and one perpendicular to it. Corresponding to

$$T = T_1 T_2,$$

where $T_1$ is a translation along the axis of rotation and $T_2$ is one perpendicular to it, we get

$$F = T_1 T_2 R.$$

We now consider $T_2 R$ on a certain plane $E$ which is perpendicular to the axis of rotation. The plane is mapped onto itself by $T_2$ and $R$, and hence also by $T_2 R$. $T_2 R$ is a plane displacement there. Since $F$ should not be a translation, $R \neq I$; the plane displacement $T_2 R$ in $E$ is thus a rotation there and has a fixed point $b$. Thus $T_2 R$ is a three-dimensional displacement with the fixed point $b$, i.e. a three-dimensional rotation $R_1$. The point $b$ and the plane $E$ are carried onto themselves by $R_1$. Thus $R_1$'s axis of rotation is perpendicular to $E$.

$$F = T_1 R_1,$$

where the translation $T_1$ is along $R_1$'s axis of rotation. There is thus a rotation and then a displacement along the axis of rotation. This is called a *screw displacement*. Translations are special cases of screw displacements (the angle of rotation is 0), just as rotations are special screw displacements (the translation arrow is a point). We saw that *all displacements are screw displacements*.

236

It is clear that each screw displacement is a displacement.
Finally, we still have to examine those congruences which
are not displacements. We already know the reflections and
seek the rest,

$$F = S_3 S_2 S_1.$$

If the planes $S_1$, $S_2$, $S_3$ are all parallel, there is a plane $S_4$
such that
$$S_3 S_2 = S_4 S_1,$$
$$\text{and so} \quad F = S_4 S_1 S_1 = S_4,$$

a reflection. So we may assume that the planes are not all
parallel, say $S_1, S_2$ intersect (the other case is treated
similarly). Through their line of intersection there is a plane
$S_2'$ perpendicular to $S_3$ and a plane $S_1'$ such that

$$S_2 S_1 = S_2' S_1',$$
$$\text{and hence} \quad F = S_3 S_2' S_1',$$

where $S_3$ and $S_2'$ are perpendicular. In the pencil of $S_2'$ and
$S_3$ there is a plane $S_3'$ which is perpendicular to $S_1'$, and $S_2''$
such that
$$S_3 S_2' = S_3' S_2'';$$

we must make sure that not only $S_2'$, $S_3$, but also $S_2''$, $S_3'$
are mutually perpendicular. We then have

$$F = S_3' S_2'' S_1',$$

where $S_3'$ is perpendicular to $S_1'$ and to $S_2''$.

$S_2'' S_1'$ is either a translation, whose translation arrows are
parallel to $S_3'$, or a rotation whose axis (the intersection of
$S_1'$, $S_2''$) is perpendicular to $S_3'$. We call the former again a

*glide reflection*, the latter a *rotary reflection*.

To produce a glide reflection, a translation is thus first carried out, and then a reflection in a plane containing a translation arrow. A rotary reflection is first a rotation and then a reflection in a plane perpendicular to the axis of rotation. Reflections are special cases of both.

Hence we have

Theorem: *Three-dimensional displacements are screw displacements. The remaining congruences are glide reflections and rotary reflections.*

In the plane, we could see whether a congruence is a displacement or not by whether or not it preserves angles. Is there something similar in three dimensions? We shall have to make a considerable digression before answering this question.


## Orientation

We begin with a one-dimensional world, the straight line. It is given a structure by means of the concept of distance. Two points on the straight line have in the usual way a distance. This is called a metric structure. The mappings which preserve the structure, the *automorphisms* of the structure, as one says, are the translations and reflections in points. They form a group, the group of automorphisms of this structure. The translations form a subgroup. Is there something which is preserved by the translations, but not by the other automorphisms?

There is on the straight line another, more basic structure, the *order structure*. Position on the straight line can be distinguished as left and right, or if thinking of the time axis, as before and after. What is actually called left, and what right, is arbitrary. Once this has been decided, the straight line is *oriented*. The orientation can be given by an arrow which points from left to right. Moreover, one only needs to know which of two points is the left and which the right. It is then known for all other pairs of points and the straight line is thereby oriented.

A straight line can be oriented in two ways. If, in one orientation, $a$ lies to the left of $b$, in the other, $b$ lies to the left of $a$. The two orientations of a straight line are opposite to each other.

What is now the difference between translations and reflections? Under translations the orientation is maintained, under reflections it is reversed.

If both structures, the metric and the order structures, are simultaneously superimposed on a straight line, the group of automorphisms is restricted, only the translations remaining. The group of automorphisms of the metric straight line is that of the translations and reflections, that of the metric, oriented straight line consists of the translations.

We go over to the two-dimensional world of the plane, with the usual distance metric structure. The group of automorphisms consist of translations, rotations and glide reflections. Can an order structure also be superimposed on the plane?

If one stands on the plane, one can form a straight line

with one's outstretched arms, which is oriented, say, from left to right. Provided one only moves along this straight line, one can satisfy oneself with that order. On the time axis one can do nothing else; one cannot turn round on it. In the plane one can step off the straight line, turn round and move about, and in so doing take the orientation along, by means of one's outstretched arms. If one then returns to the original straight line, one may notice that the designated straight line has now a new orientation, the other one, superimposed on it. At the same time, however, something else has changed, the line of sight, the distinction between 'back' and 'front'. In the plane, the distinction between 'left' and 'right' has meaning only if combined with the distinction between 'back' and 'front'. The combination of these two distinctions is the distinction between 'anticlockwise' and 'clockwise'. 'Anticlockwise' means that the *right* arm should swing *forward*.

To *orientate* the plane means to say what is 'anticlockwise' and what is 'clockwise'. This can be done in many ways. The most immediate one is to orientate *one* straight line and to specify which of its sides is *in front*. This then extends to all oriented lines. To be sure, after the walk in the plane I can find 'front' and 'back' interchanged, but then 'left' and 'right' are, too. However, 'anticlockwise' has remained 'anticlockwise'. The orientation of the plane can also be given by two intersecting oriented straight lines; the first one distinguishes between 'left' and 'right', the second, between 'back' and 'front' (it points from the rear side to the forward side). But in this, it is important which is the first and which the second line.

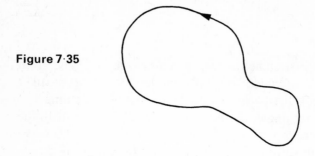

**Figure 7·35**

It can also be done with a closed figure in which an arrow is inserted. See figure 7·35.

Exactly two oriented planes correspond to each unoriented one. The automorphisms of the unoriented, metric plane are the translations, rotations and glide reflections; on the oriented one, the glide reflections are excluded, since if one stands on the reflecting line, 'left' and 'right' are certainly preserved under reflection, but 'front' and 'rear' are interchanged. Perpendicular to it, exactly the reverse takes place, but in any case the orientation is altered.

The orientation structure of the plane is no luxury. It is needed, for example, in order to know how to turn the coffee mill. Euclid neglected it. He always works in the unoriented plane, and out of loyalty to tradition it is still done at school in this way. Euclid did not know about coffee mills, but the omission was even at that time unpractical for other reasons. It affects the *concept of angle*. Euclid always reckons angles as positive, from 0° to 180° (he said it somewhat differently, since he didn't talk about degrees). All right angles are the same to Euclid. But to the surveyor and astronomer they are not the same. If they set up a right angle on the meridian and do it to the wrong side, something goes wrong. If, starting from the equator, they mark off a quadrant of a circle on the meridian, it can come either to the celestial north or south pole. It is of assistance here to use east and west longitudes, south and north latitudes, but this is inelegant and unsuitable.

However, a day came when the semicircular protractor was replaced by the circular protractor, without bothering to specify new instructions for use. The instructions are quite simple for a semicircular protractor. Place it so that one arm of the angle (it does not matter which) goes through the zero of the scale and the other meets the semicircle; at the meeting point, the size of the angle is read off. With a circular protractor one has first of all to distinguish between the two arms of the angle. One has to state explicitly which so to speak is the fixed arm of the angle and which the moving arm. The fixed arm passes through the zero and the angle size is read off at the moving arm. If they are interchanged, an angle say of 90° becomes one of 270° or −90°. This is not all, however. If I turn the (transparent) protractor over, the same mishap occurs. How can I prevent this? Now, there are numbers on the protractor. I suggest placing it so that the 2 appears as 2 and not as its mirror image. But I can only distinguish the 2 from its image in an oriented plane. The circular protractor is only usuable in an oriented plane.

Yet these instructions for use are still not quite right. After all, I do not sit in the plane when I use it, but in three dimensions. And from which side should I consider the protractor?

With this we come to the question of the orientation of space. The distinction between 'left turn' and 'right turn' of the oriented plane breaks down just as the distinction between 'left' and 'right' did in the transition from the straight line to the plane. Usually we do not notice this, since we live by and large on a plane, the surface of the earth. The command 'to the left' is uniquely understood, since everybody knows that it is to be carried out on one's feet and not on one's head. Should it occur to anyone to turn to his left while standing on his head, the onlookers would declare that he was turning to his right. (Anybody who doesn't believe it can try it out. At his own risk, of course.) To save you the danger, I recommend you an experiment: take a four-colour pencil. Place it in front of you and rotate it to the left (if you don't know what 'to the left' is, you need only turn it between the palms of your hands, so that you move your right forward and your left backwards – you surely know what your right hand is). On my pencil the colour indicators then follow in the order red, black, green, blue. If you place the pencil on its top, and carry out the same action, the cycle proceeds in the reversed order. In both cases you have rotated the pencil to the left, but the pencil, if it could speak, would call one a rotation to the left and the other a rotation to the right. Imagine a dancer instead of the pencil: when he waltzes anticlockwise, you see consecutively his face, his right ear, his back and his left ear. If he did this on his head, exactly the opposite would happen.

The meaning of 'clockwise' and 'anticlockwise' thus depends on the concepts of 'top' and 'bottom'. The distinction between 'top' and 'bottom' usually speaks for itself. 'To the left' is naturally not to be interpreted while standing on your head. The coffee mill is rotated clockwise, according to the directions for use, and in so doing we obviously don't put it on its top, since then the coffee beans would fall out. It gets harder when two people stand opposite each other and are supposed to turn a wheel or a grindstone clockwise. They won't achieve very much, since each considers that side of the wheel where he stands as the top. The distinction between 'anticlockwise' and 'clockwise' only has meaning in three dimensions, if it is connected with the distinction between 'top' and 'bottom'. One must explain which side of the wheel's surface is to be considered as below and which as above. In other words, it is necessary to add an orientation of the axis, an arrow pointing from the bottom to the top. As soon as this *axis arrow* is doubtful, the concepts of 'clockwise' and 'anticlockwise' lose their meaning. Paint a 2 on the window pane. Yes, but from the outside or the inside? The start of the number 2 is a curve to the right – yes, but seen from which point of view? (Now think about the exact directions for use of the circular protractor on an oriented plane in space.)

The linking of the distinction between 'clockwise' and 'anticlockwise' with the distinction between 'top' and 'bottom', of the direction of rotation with the axis arrow, leads to the orientation of space. Now there are objects which incorporate this link: screws and corkscrews. A screw in front of you is *right-handed* if the thread runs from the *bottom left* to the *top right*. This definition is independent of your position relative to the screw. You may run around in order to look at it from the back, and you may stand on your head. (But rather turn the screw round!) The right-handed screw is a combination of 'clockwise' and 'inwards' ('downwards') or of 'anticlockwise' and 'outwards' ('upwards'). If I replace 'clockwise' by 'anticlockwise' *or* 'inwards' by 'outwards', the right-handed screw becomes a left-handed screw; if I replace both at the same time, it remains a right-handed screw. I cannot say whether the rotating earth or a rotating electron are turning clockwise or anticlockwise. The answer depends on how I direct the axis of rotation. The rotating earth does not orientate space either. If I add the axis arrow (from the south to the north pole) to the rotation and stipulate 'this is to be a left-handed screw', space is then oriented.

The straight line was oriented in so far as I took one of two points and said 'this one is on the left'. The plane was oriented in so far as I gave a certain direction of rotation the name 'anticlockwise'. *Space* is *oriented* by the production of a screw, to be called a left-handed screw. Instead of a screw, one can also take an oriented plane whose two sides are distinguished as bottom and top or as negative and positive, or through which an arrow passes. It can also be done with three perpendicular, oriented straight lines $x_1$, $x_2$, $x_3$ through a point; in the $x_1x_2$-plane we then define the direction of rotation of the movement from $x_1$ to $x_2$ through 90°, and we take the $x_3$-direction as axis. It can also be done with a spinning top. I mean by this a circular disc whose circumference is oriented and through which an arrow is stuck perpendicularly (figure 7·36). A knot also determines a screw-direction: consider for example the screw displacement with which you start to tie a bow (right-handed people tie clock-

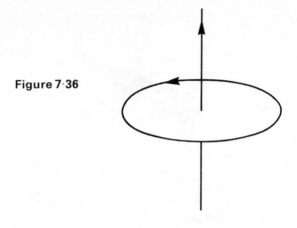

**Figure 7·36**

wise). In any case, however, when one has demonstrated the screw, one must specify which is the right (or positive) screw-direction. (Some people call the left screw-direction positive.)

There are two oriented, metric spaces corresponding to the unoriented one. A left-handed screw in one is called a right-handed screw in the other, and vice versa.

The automorphisms of the usual metric space are the screw displacements, glide reflections and rotary reflections. In oriented space, only the screw displacements remain. A right-handed screw becomes a left-handed screw in a mirror: if its axis lies in the plane of the mirror, because the direction of rotation is reversed, and if it is perpendicular to the plane of the mirror, because the axis arrow is reversed.

Now, does one need *unoriented* or *oriented* space for a *description of nature*?

Naturally, we need oriented space. In unoriented space we couldn't even use corkscrews to open wine bottles. The physicist too needs it, since how otherwise should he screw

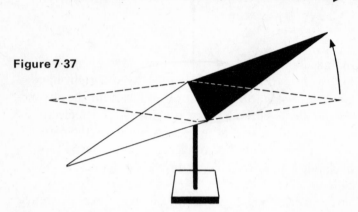

**Figure 7·37**

in a fuse or a contact screw? Nor can the biochemist do without it, if he wants to distinguish the L-compounds, which occur in living organisms, from the D-compounds, which are symmetric to them.

But is not this accidental? Couldn't the corkscrews and screwdrivers have been constructed in the opposite way, and couldn't life have developed also with D-compounds?

In nature there is a screw direction *de facto*. But is there also one *de iure*? Does one also need oriented space to formulate the general laws of nature? Now, in mechanics we certainly don't need it, but what about in electromagnetism? In this subject there is after all the so-called *corkscrew rule*. When electricity flows through a conductor above (or below) a magnetic needle (figure 7·37), the magnetic needle is deflected it wants to come to rest perpendicular to the current. The following rule gives the side to which it is deflected: imagine a (right-handed) corkscrew with its axis in the wire and screwed in the (conventional) direction of current; then the north pole of the magnetic needle is deflected as if it is struck by the handle of the corkscrew. Does this then mean a right-handed corkscrew *de iure*, as a law of nature? It certainly seems so. If I have forgotten what a right-handed corkscrew is, I ask nature a question and wait for the answer: I carry out the mentioned experiment, i.e. I let electricity flow over the magnetic needle; according to the needle's deflection and by using the corkscrew rule I determine what a right-handed corkscrew is. Nature thus defines a definite screw direction. But beware!

In order to draw conclusions, I must answer two questions: first, which is the direction of current, secondly, where is the magnetic needle's *north pole*? Both are arbitrarily, but firmly, defined. The electric current of a torch battery flows from the zinc to the carbon; I thus only need to open the battery to find out the direction of current. The north pole of a magnetic needle points north, at least at most places on Earth. If I want to find out where the north pole of a magnetic needle is, I thus must know where north is on Earth. The rule is of no use far from Earth. If, on a journey through the universe, I ask nature that question, I certainly get an answer again, but one which I can't make meaningful. Now it is usual here on Earth to blacken the north half of the magnetic needle and to leave the south half blank. If I take such a needle with me on my journey, I can apply the corkscrew rule everywhere in order to calibrate screws as right and left.

But now let us suppose that we wish to tell the physicists of distant worlds what a right-handed screw means to us. We are in radio contact with them, we have translated our earthly physics into theirs and theirs into ours, and we want to define a right-handed screw for them – define theoretically and not just demonstrate it. Thus, for example, we wouldn't specify a chance star configuration which moves like a right-handed screw. Nor, say, send them circularly polarised light accompanied by an explanation of the direction in which it is polarised. How should we do it? It doesn't work with the corkscrew rule of electricity theory, since how should we tell them there what the north pole of a magnetic needle is?

Again, knowledge of the right-handed screw direction is indispensable for opening wine bottles, for screwing fuses, for knowing how the vault of heaven rotates, for electromagnetic experiments, but it is a *screw direction* which in the last resort can *only be shown, not theoretically defined*. This is best made clear by setting oneself the task of telling (not showing) physicists in distant worlds what a right-handed screw is.

At least, that is what one still thought a few years ago. It was a dogma which no physicist doubted. But in the meantime a discovery has been made which may well be the most important contribution to the study of space since the theory of relativity. Magnets have been discovered in which the north pole is distinguished by law; of course, not such crude magnets as in our compasses and the marking of the north pole is not done with paint.

The magnets I mean are *radioactive atomic nuclei*. Atomic nuclei in general behave like spinning tops; in positive nuclei it is positive electricity that rotates, and such a circular current makes the nucleus appear as a magnet. But a spinning top without an axis arrow still doesn't define a screw. And a magnet without an indicated north pole doesn't help us further.

If a nucleus isn't stable, but is $\beta$-radioactive, it can emit an electron, and the directions of emission can give us the missing arrows. At least, provided they are not all perpendicular to the magnet's axis or equally divided between 'up' and 'down'.

Eight years ago an experiment was carried out on $^{60}$Co and it appeared that emission took place in certain preferred directions, which formed a left-handed screw with the direction of rotation of the nucleus. In other words, it appeared that the $^{60}$Co magnets carry an indicator at their south pole, namely that of the *preferred direction of emission*.

Naturally, the labelled magnets weren't accidentally or blindly hit upon. A doubt had arisen in the minds of the Sino-American physicists Lee and Yang during fundamental investigations into the decay of mesons, the doubt about the dogma that the orientation of space is not theoretically definable. The doubt materialised in the experiment that was carried out at their suggestion. In retrospect, their result can be formulated in a widely understandable way. But the profound considerations were historically necessary, since this result would never have been believed before.

If we wish to tell physicists somewhere in the universe *de iure* what we mean by a right-handed corkscrew, we only need telegraph to them:

'In $^{60}$Co nuclei the direction of rotation together with the preferred direction of emission of $\beta$-electrons forms a left-handed screw.'

They can then repeat the experiment which Lee and Yang suggested eight years ago, and by means of the result,

250

combined with the corkscrew rule of electricity theory, translate our earthly terms 'right' and 'left'. We can thus tell (not show) the inhabitants of distant worlds what 'right' and 'left' are. There is, however, a difficulty.

Suppose their $^{60}$Co nuclei are right-handed, not left-handed corkscrews. That is indeed conceivable and would be the case if their world is an *antiworld*. Our physical world is built very unsymmetrically. Our electrons, the light elementary particles, are nearly all negatively charged. Positive ones are rare in our world and they don't last long, since if they hit a negative one, they cancel each other out. Nearly all our heavy charged particles, the protons, are positive: they, too, cancel out the few negative colleagues they meet. It has long been suspected that the preponderance of negative electrons and positive protons is something like a local tradition of our part of the universe. Elsewhere the 'antiparticles' could play the role which the 'particles' play here. The boundary between world and antiworld would then be a battlefield of the protons and electrons. In the antiworld $^{60}$Co would consist of negative protons and positive electrons. The $^{60}$Co magnets would be 'wrongly' marked there; they would statistically define right-handed instead of left-handed corkscrews.[2] If our physicists think they can tell the physicists there what right-handed screws are, they are indulging in

2 One might think that in the anti-world physicists would interpret our corkscrew rule the other way round, since in antitorch batteries there is antizinc and anticarbon, and hence the current flows in the opposite direction; one should remember, however, that the magnets also consist of antiiron, and this cancels the reversal.

narrow-minded provincialism. The language of their world is after all only a dialect which is not understood in the antiworld (not at least until it is known that the messages are coming from a world built in the reverse way).

The question which occupied us here can be formulated more precisely as follows: is it possible, in the space where we live, to give a *verbal definition* which specifies what right- and left-handed screws are, in such a way of course that in every possible case the result agrees with our everyday, non-theoretical, concept which depends on demonstration. The answer to this question about the *de iure* definability of a right-handed screw depends, as we saw, on the *de facto* structure of the cosmos (which probably in the last resort is again a *de iure* structure).

# Acknowledgments

Acknowledgment is due to the following for the illustrations (the number refers to the page on which the illustration appears): frontispiece The Warburg Institute, London; 11 *L'Illustration*; 43 The Eccleston Hotel, London; 61 J. B. Wolters' Uitgeversmaatschappij N.V., Groningen; 123 Flatters and Garnett Ltd; 139 The National Maritime Museum, London; 165 and 197 The Mansell Collection.

The diagrams were drawn by Design Practitioners Limited.

Certain parts of chapter 3 are taken from a lecture which Professor Freudenthal gave at the Palais de la Découverte, Paris, in 1952, and which is available from the library of the Palais as a pamphlet entitled *Machines Pensantes*.

Some books published or in preparation

## Economics and Social Studies

**The World Cities**
Peter Hall, *London*

**The Economics of Underdeveloped Countries**
Jagdish Bhagwati, *Delhi*

**Development Planning**
Jan Tinbergen, *Rotterdam*

**Decisive Forces in World Economics**
J. L. Sampedro, *Madrid*

**Key Issues in Criminology**
Roger Hood, *Durham*

**Human Communication**
J. L. Aranguren, *Madrid*

**Education in the Modern World**
John Vaizey, *London*

## History

**The Emergence of Greek Democracy**
W. G. Forrest, *Oxford*

**Muhammad and the Conquests of Islam**
Francesco Gabrieli, *Rome*

**Humanism in the Renaissance**
S. Dresden, *Leyden*

**The Ottoman Empire**
Halil Inalcik, *Ankara*

**The Rise of Toleration**
Henry Kamen, *Warwick*

**The Left in Europe**
David Caute, *Oxford*

**The Rise of the Working Class**
Jürgen Kuczynski, *Berlin*

**Chinese Communism**
Robert C. North, *Stanford*

## Philosophy and Religion

**Christianity**
W. O. Chadwick, *Cambridge*

**Monasticism**
David Knowles, *London*

**Judaism**
J. Soetendorp, *Amsterdam*

**The Modern Papacy**
K. O. von Aretin, *Gottingen*

**Sects**
Bryan Wilson, *Oxford*

## Language and Literature

**A Model of Language**
E. M. Uhlenbeck, *Leyden*

**French Literature**
Raymond Picard, *Paris*

**Russian Writers and Society**
Ronald Hingley, *Oxford*

**Satire**
Matthew Hodgart, *Sussex*

## The Arts

**Primitive Art**
Eike Haberland, *Mainz*

**The Language of Modern Art**
Ulf Linde, *Stockholm*

**Aesthetic Theories since 1850**
J. F. Revel, *Paris*

**Art Nouveau**
S. T. Madsen, *Oslo*

**Academic Painting**
Gerald Ackerman, *Stanford*

**Palaeolithic Cave Art**
P. J. Ucko and A. Rosenfeld, *London*

## Psychology and Human Biology

**Eye and Brain**
R. L. Gregory, *Cambridge*

**The Ear and the Brain**
Edward Carterette, *U.C.L.A.*

**The Variety of Man**
J. P. Garlick, *London*

**The Biology of Work**
O. G. Edholm, *London*

**Psychoses**
H. J. Bochnik, *Hamburg*

**Child Development**
Philippe Muller, *Neuchâtel*

**Man and Disease**
Gernot Rath, *Göttingen*

**Chinese Medicine**
P. Huard and M. Wong, *Paris*

**The Psychology of Fear and Stress**
J. A. Gray, *Oxford*

## Zoology and Botany

**Animal Communication**
J. M. Cullen, *Oxford*

**Mimicry**
Wolfgang Wickler, *Seewiesen*

**Migration**
Gustaf Rudebeck, *Stockholm*

**The World of an Insect**
Rémy Chauvin, *Strasbourg*

**Biological Rhythms**
Janet Harker, *Cambridge*

**Lower Animals**
Martin Wells, *Cambridge*

**Dinosaurs**
Bjöon Kurtén, *Helsinki*

## Physical Science and Mathematics

**Mathematics Observed**
H. Freudenthal, *Utrecht*

**The Quest for Absolute Zero**
K. Mendelssohn, *Oxford*

**Particles and Accelerators**
Robert Gouiran, *C.E.R.N., Geneva*

**Optics**
A. C. S. van Heel and
C. H. F. Velzel, *Eindhoven*

**Waves and Corpuscles**
J. L. Andrade e Silva and
G. Lochak, *Paris*
Introduction by Louis de Broglie

**Energy**
J. Fischhoff, *Paris*

## Earth Sciences and Astronomy

**The Electrical Earth**
J. Sayers, *Birmingham*

**Climate and Weather**
H. Flohn, *Bonn*

**The Structure of the Universe**
E. L. Schatzman, *Paris*

## Applied Science

**Words and Waves**
A. H. W. Beck, *Cambridge*

**The Science of Decision-Making**
A. Kaufmann, *Paris*

**Bioengineering**
H. S. Wolff, *London*

**Bionics**
Lucien Gerardin, *Paris*

**Metals and Civilisation**
R. W. Cahn, *Sussex*